BELLY DANCING
IS NOT A SPECTATOR SPORT

If your idea of belly dancing is based on foreign tempt-resses performing in smoked-filled dens of iniquity, you're in for a surprise. Thousands of women of all ages from every part of the country are already par-ticipating in belly dancing classes. They're enjoying themselves while they slim down.

Not long ago a prominent politician's daughter made headlines with her belly dancing debut. And another politician, on a recent visit abroad, was photographed at a belly dancing exhibition. He looked delighted. His wife just looked. Maybe she didn't realize that belly dancing is no longer a spectator sport. Don't *you* stay on the sidelines. Join in the fun.

BELLY DANCING IS FOR YOU

THE ART OF BELLY DANCING

DAHLENA

With Dona Z. Meilach

*This low-priced Bantam Book
has been completely reset in a type face
designed for easy reading, and was printed
from new plates. It contains the complete
text of the original hard-cover edition.*
NOT ONE WORD HAS BEEN OMITTED.

THE ART OF BELLY DANCING
A Bantam Book / February 1975

Published simultaneously in the United States and Canada

*Bantam Books are published by Bantam Books, Inc. Its trade-
mark, consisting of the words "Bantam Books" and the
portrayal of a bantam, is registered in the United States
Patent Office and in other countries. Marca Registrada. Bantam
Books, Inc., 666 Fifth Avenue, New York, New York 10019.*

PRINTED IN THE UNITED STATES OF AMERICA
0 9 8 7 6

For Angela and Joseph

ACKNOWLEDGMENTS

We are indebted to many people who helped to make this book so much fun to develop:

- To Dahlena's students, who permitted us to take informal class photographs.
- To the dancers, whose performances and costumes are a beautiful counterpoint to the exercises: Barbara Cargill (Natasha), Cheryl Johnson (Dena), Kathy Lappa (Helena), Maya Marzullo (Maya), Jane Coles (Jaña), Nadia and others.
- To Jimmy Payne, who graciously permitted us to use his dance studio for our photography sessions.
- To Seymon Francos, The Athens North, Chicago, Illinois, for providing a stage where students can perform and for encouraging the dance as the art form it is.
- To Joe Lazar and Tony Karagozian, for their musical expertise and advice.
- To Ibrahim Farrah for advice on finger cymbal patterns.
- To Dr. Melvin Meilach and Seymour Zweigoron, for their invaluable assistance during the photo sessions.
- To Paul Banks, for his definitive drawings.
- To Ben Lavitt, Astra Photo Service, Chicago, Illinois, and his staff, for their interest beyond duty in processing the photos.
- To Marilyn Regula, for patiently deciphering our scribbled rough drafts into a perfectly typewritten manuscript.

To all of you, our eternal gratitude and praise.

Dahlena, Chicago, Illinois
Dona Meilach, Palos Heights, Illinois

CONTENTS

CHAPTER 1

THE ART OF BELLY DANCING

Until recently, the mere mention of belly dancing elicited predictable responses. Women would snicker; men would wiggle raised brows over lasciviously glazed eyes. Most people would think of Greek restaurants and swirling, swishing hips. A few might conjure up a vision of a diaphanously adorned, glistening girl gliding about a fat sultan.

If you have one of the stereotyped images, it's time to take a new look. Belly dancing is rapidly checking its tarnished aura. Its gold coins and bangles are sparkling brightly, proudly, haughtily.

Belly dancing, as an ancient art form reborn, has come of age—spinning frenziedly into the limelight as a healthy, exciting body conditioner and a beautiful dance. Women of every age throughout the country are signing up for the burgeoning numbers of classes held in YMCA and park district gymnasiums, university recreation classes, private dance studios, and by such unlikely sponsors as church and temple self-improvement programs.

What motivates a woman to enroll in a belly dance class? Ask some of your neighbors. Many are already

1

stretching to the strains of exotic Middle Eastern melodies. Their answers will sound something like this:

"It seemed fun, different, daring. And exotic. It is."

"It's such a feminine form of exercise. I love to dance and the combination is super."

"At 30, my tummy was popped like a beach ball from three pregnancies. I've gotten it into shape and am unashamedly wearing bikinis again."

"After an auto accident my shoulders were so stiff my doctor prescribed therapy. I saw a friend exercising for the snake arm movement and I did it too. Now my shoulders move like they're greased and I've never felt more toned up in my life."

"I'm not an athlete and I couldn't keep up with my husband's tennis. A belly dance class was convenient; now it's a way of life. My husband would rather watch me practice than play an extra set of mixed doubles."

Whether you need exercise to get back into shape after having a baby, or you want to create an Arabiannights atmosphere for one favorite sultan, you'll discover that belly dancing is the magical, aphrodisiacal answer to most women's dreams of keeping their bodies in trim.

And what bonuses! Your torso firms up if you're flabby and rounds out in the right places if you're thin. Your posture will improve; you'll hold your head high, chest up and out, and tummy in. You'll unconsciously develop a subtle, wondrous wiggle to your hips. You'll be more flexible and your circulation—both kinds—will improve.

Yes. Belly dancing can make you more popular. It

adds a twinkle to your eye and zest to your personality. When someone asks, "what are you doing lately?" your casual answer, "belly dancing," often results in an incredulous stare. It's a conversation opener for any occasion, and if you know a little about Middle Eastern culture, the food and the music, you can keep an audience spellbound with your worldly wisdom. Many women sign up for a class "only for the exercise." Soon they are hemming a veil, making a practice skirt, and cooking Turkish and Greek dishes.

Belly dancing origins are shrouded in almost as much mystery as the veiled dancer tries to convey. There are early Egyptian and Etruscan tomb paintings that resemble later Middle Eastern dancers. In India, stone sculptures—from the first century B.C. to the fourth century A.D.—of sensually posed and partially draped maidens have a peculiar similarity to belly dance positions. The first-century Roman poet, Juvenal, wrote of dancing girls in Cadiz as "sinking down with quivering thighs to the floor." Martial, another Roman poet, described dancers who "with endless prurience swing lascivious loins in practiced writhings."

Yakshi, from the East Gate of the Great Stupa, Sanchi, India, dates from about the first century B.C. with a pose like that of a belly dancer—rib cage and hips out.

Dahlena practices the Camel Walk with her students.

More recent history traces belly dancing back a few centuries to the Middle Eastern cultures, with varying styles emanating from different Arabic countries and from Turkey and Greece. In these countries the dance, referred to as "Middle Eastern" or "oriental," is an expression of the music and of the people. It is more often a folk dance, a part of the ethnic culture, and the sensual element is definitely subdued. Young girls of good families learn the movements by mimicking their elders. They may perform for their families and for guests. "Sometimes, for the fun of it," reports one Egyptian woman, "several girl friends of a bride-to-be will dance for the groom the night before his wedding."

Another variation of the belly dance is related to the amatory arts learned by ladies of the harem and professional entertainers. These dancers rely heavily on pelvic and muscular movements. The third variation, referred to as the "cabaret" style, combines the folk and harem dance, but, if the dancer is well trained, the dance is done more gracefully and with more movement about the stage.

Through the years, this dance has been badly abused by the cabaret world which has unabashedly

4

billed it as suggestive and sexual. Too often, the dancers themselves exceed the boundaries of good taste. The elegant performance of the belly dance is not meant to be sexual. The correct word would be sensual. In this respect, it is no different from most dancing.

Belly dancing must be approached in the same way as every other art form—painting, sculpture, or music: it can be accomplished on many different levels, and its lowest form can barely resemble its highest form. At its best, the dance is the result of a discipline that demands a perfect concentration and coordination between mind and body.

This high level of artistic discipline gives the dance the classical image it deserves—the image that is emanating today and is greatly responsible for the increasing popularity of belly dancing. The dancer moves only to show her audience the beauty of the undulating movements and to interpret the mood of music, which ranges from gay and happy to painful, mournful, and sad. This is also why the ballerina dons her tutu and toe shoes and the Tahitian dancer her grass skirt.

Probably the growth of the belly dance as a serious art has been hampered by its earthy title. This was planted in the Western vocabulary when a group of dancers was brought to the U.S. in 1893 for the Chicago Columbian Exposition. When the public learned that the literal translation of the French phrase *danse du ventre* was "belly dance," they concluded that it was salacious and immoral. The star of the show was billed as Little Egypt, and the dance movements, which originally stemmed from the Middle East, were thereafter dubbed "belly dancing." The young promotor, Sol Bloom, knew that these events meant an entertainment gold mine. Later, he wrote in his autobiography, "It is regrettable that more people remembered the reputation of the *danse du ventre* than the dance itself. . . . While sensual and exciting, it was a masterpiece of rhythm and beauty. It was choreographic perfection."

For many years, enthusiasm for belly dancing was centered mainly in nightclubs and cabarets in the Western world. An occasional movie and a few dancers propelled it into a brief spotlight in such performances as the opera *Salome* in Chicago in 1910. Mary Garden's famous *Dance of the Seven Veils* so stunned the audience and brought such quick publicity that the promoters closed voluntarily before the police forcibly shut the doors. When the performance became a success in Milwaukee, other dancers, much less artful than Miss Garden, borrowed the veil concept to peddle the idea of a fleshy, superseductive dance that was eventually denigrated to a cliché striptease act. Thus was the art of belly dancing dropped into a tawdry quagmire of unabashed sexual suggestiveness.

By the late 1920s, belly dancing again became popular in Cairo nightclubs, and dancers carried their performances to other parts of the world. Still, the graceful, controlled body movements remained an outcast from the world of the serious dancer and the respectable dance studio. Arab and other Middle Eastern nice girls continued to perform it as a folk dance, but there was no mingling, no exchange of ideas between these upper-class girls and the cabaret performers who were considered the lowest type of women.

Interestingly, Arabs today in many countries perform these same dance movements at their weddings. When the nuptials are over and the music begins, men and women gather on the dance floor and obviously enjoy their national dance with the same feeling that the Israelis do the sherilah, the Polish do the polka, the Russians the kazatsky, and the Irish the jig. To the Arabs, Turks, Greeks, and others, this Middle Eastern dance, with only slightly different cultural variations, is the physical expression of the musical strains that weave a magic spell.

Belly dancers have appeared in
various versions of *Salome,
Scheherazade,* and other operas
and ballets. Leon Bakst, a well-
known stage designer, created
this costume for a Syrian dancer
in the ballet *Cleopatra.*

What barriers have been broken so that the Western dancer has suddenly embraced the belly dance? Why has it become so respectable that you and you and you are anxious to set your hips gyrating, your tummy fluttering, and all of you rolling, sepentine fashion, on the floor?

It may be because of our increasingly smaller world, our eagerness to understand the peoples of every culture. It may be our own change in mores. It may also be that Western man has dug deeply into the religious philosophy and spirituality of the East and discovered that the dance, too, requires an almost metaphysical concentration and discipline.

No matter what the answer, the fact is that the Middle Eastern dance is a marvelous physical and emotional experience. It frees you from your everyday, mundane routine. It may set your mind to dreaming of faraway places, of cultures that have much to offer. It gives you an opportunity to acquaint yourself with your body, to achieve a new sense of freedom.

Yes, the belly dance, or Middle Eastern or oriental dance—whatever you want to call it—has become virtuous and respectable. It has emerged from its cocoon and is being admired as the beautiful butterfly that it is.

CHAPTER 2

LIMBERING UP AND DANCE BASICS

Belly dancing requires training to strengthen the muscles so the body will move the way you want it to. This training firms up flesh, trims your figure, straightens your posture, and gives you a new wake-up and look-alive feeling. It enables you to transform the simplest movement into a controlled dance step. The exercises are fun. The results promise your doing a dance that some consider naughty but nice. What a departure from the counting out of boring calisthenics!

Once the muscles are disciplined, the movements become graceful, sinuous, supple. What is involved? In both the exercises and the dance you will learn to concentrate on the following:

ISOLATING the muscles so that each portion of the body can move independently.
CONTRACTING the muscles to give them control, strength, and coordination.
STRETCHING every part of the body so you know each exists as a separate, though connected, entity.

Throughout this book, each dance step has been thoroughly studied and broken down to extract the exercises: you will be able to follow the movements clearly and logically. Concentrate at first (until your brain automatically sends messages) so that your rib cage, for example, moves out of your waist while your hips are still. You'll be astonished that parts of you can assume unprecedented positions. Study the drawing on page 14, and you'll have a better understanding of how the rib cage, pelvis, thighs, abdomen, and other parts of your body are connected by muscles. The essence of the belly dance is to learn how to isolate the rib cage from the waist, to control the abdomen and hips, and to move the shoulders independently of the elbows, wrists, and hands. Once you are accustomed to moving the muscles properly, the exercises will quickly smooth out into dance movements. Before you know it, you'll be dancing and, even more, you'll be delighted with your newfound body flexibility.

What to Wear When You Practice

The best practice costume is one that exposes the abdominal area—a two-piece leotard, or shorts and a midriff top. Wear tights to keep your legs warm. Chilled legs and muscles will often cause a stiffening rather than a limbering up.

The on-stage dancer wears shoes with heels, but, for practice, exercise in stocking feet or ballet slippers to yield the greatest stretch in legs, hips, and waist. Slippery floors make practice difficult, so use rosin or work out on a rug—especially for the floor exercises. As you progress, add a chain belt or fringe around your hips to accentuate your movements. Later on, working with a practice skirt is fun (see chapter 9).

Mirror, Mirror on the Wall

A full-length mirror to practice with can be your best ally. It will tell you when your movements are graceful and beautiful or when they are stilted and require more work. Watch your progress and observe how the muscles isolate. Compare your movements with the photos in the book. Allow elbow-bending room and ample space to move when you stretch out for the floor exercises.

Music

Ideally, music should be played while you are practicing and during limbering-up sessions. Music makes exercise more rhythmic and pleasant, especially when the exercise becomes a wonderful way of learning to dance at the same time. With a good two-two or two-four beat, you can establish a mood and rhythm. You can become accustomed to the music and listen for the beats and changing tempos.

You might begin with a popular selection, such as "Tradition" or "Matchmaker" from *Fiddler on the Roof,* "Hava Na Gila," or any rock song with a good drumbeat. Records for belly dancing, with the distinctive Middle Eastern syncopation and instruments, are readily available from record shops. A record specially developed for readers of this book offers music for slow and fast combinations; it may be ordered from the firms listed in the Supply Sources.

How to Proceed

For quickest and most satisfactory results, begin each session with the limbering-up stretches and dance basics in this chapter. They are the foundation from which you can build the controlled, fluid, graceful movements into an art form. More important, by the time these movements are a part of your routine, your body will have become firm and flexible.

All exercises and movements should be practiced slowly until you feel that the particular portion of your body you are concentrating on is responding as you want it to. Do each exercise a few times at first, then build up gradually to ten repeats or more. Some of the movements may take several practice sessions before you feel you are doing them properly. Once you have control of each section as it is broken down, gradually smooth out the exercise into a movement by running each segment into the next. These movements provide you with a simple basis for the dance combinations, described in chapter 10, that can be set to different musical tempos.

If you're tempted to peek and try some of the exercises and movements in the following chapters, by all means, do so. But don't expect to be an instant belly dancer by going through each movement once or twice. You'll be more successful if you have all the movements of this chapter well under your tummy before you seriously approach the next chapters. Form the habit of doing a few of the exercises at various times during the day. Then, as often as you can— once, twice, three times or more a week—put the exercises to twenty minutes on one side of a record. Let your movements express you and the music—slow and brooding, or fast, happy, and with abandonment. Sway, roll, enjoy.

What You Should Know About Your Body

Are you wondering if you can isolate, stretch, and contract your muscles and get firm results? Study the drawing showing the relationship of the muscles to

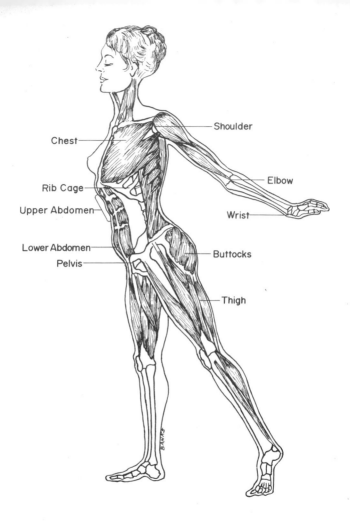

Shoulder

Chest

Rib Cage

Upper Abdomen

Lower Abdomen

Pelvis

Elbow

Wrist

Buttocks

Thigh

14

the skeleton. The muscles (in dark lines) control the movement of the bony structure. When they are in condition, they can drive the bones almost any way your mind directs. Conditioning the muscles also determines whether you have smooth contours or bulges and sagging flesh—this has nothing to do with your weight.

Muscles work together in pairs and in groups. When groups of muscles are not used, or are used too little, they tend to deteriorate and lose their tone—that is, their strength, firmness, and elasticity. Any extra fat gravitates to and settles around muscles that are not in tone. Weak, flabby muscles cannot break up the fat that nestles around them.

What does break up that fat, firm muscles, and provide the strength required to control the bones? Only exercise. The particular exercises extracted from the belly dance will promote optimum results for renewing your body so it is flexible, smooth, and strong.

Now to begin.

THE BODY STRETCH

The Body Stretch is an overall waker-upper for sluggish muscles. You'll feel your rib cage pull up and away from your hips. Do each part of this exercise for a few minutes before every session until you are limber enough to swing the bent torso smoothly from side to side.

A. Feet slightly apart. Clasp hands behind your back. Pull up and forward with your chin and chest. Really stretch your arms back and your torso way out until you feel the bottom of your rib cage pull up and away from your abdomen. Tuck in the buttocks. Hold for five counts. Repeat.

16

B. Bend over the left leg.
Stretch and hold. Move to
center. Hold, and then bend
over the right leg. Hold.
Repeat at least five times until
you can slowly swing your
torso from side to side.

C. In the center position, head
up, hands on legs at a height
where your *back* is *straight*.
Suck the stomach in and up.
Hold. Then push it out slowly
and repeat several times.

17

RIB CAGE ISOLATION

The rib cage, the bony structure in your upper torso that protects your heart, lungs, and other vital organs, has a remarkable set of muscles that few people learn to use for figure control. Isolating the rib cage leads to the undulating dance movements. As an exercise, it tends to thin out the abdomen and waist and to improve your posture.

A. First, learn the proper position and stretch. Place hands at hipbones. Push back against your hips with your hands. *Stretch* your chest up and out.

B. Hold the rib cage up, then concentrate on your lower torso. *Contract* the buttocks, tilt the pelvis, and bring your navel back toward your spine. Repeat A and B at least four times. Stretch, hold, contract, hold. With the chest up and buttocks contracted in, you are ready to slide the rib cage.

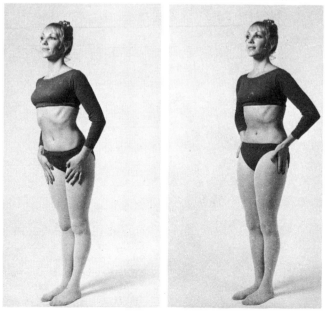

C. Place hands at sides of hips. Push right hand against right hip. Pull the rib cage to the *right side*.

D. Push the left hand against the left hip. Pull the rib cage to the *left side*.

DO NOT drop shoulder and weight from side to side.

DO NOT pull with the shoulder or move the head or hips.

DO concentrate on the lower part of the rib cage.

DO work the rib cage around in a smooth circle, first one way and then the other, after you have practiced pulling it from side to side and front to back at least ten times.

E. Pull the rib cage *forward* while you push back against your hips. Always contract the buttocks tightly; do not arch your back.

F. Relax your hands, keep your stomach contracted, and push your rib cage *back*.

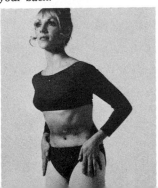

LIMB STRETCHES

These basic limb stretches should be part of every warm-up session. They stretch the rib cage away from the hips, slim the waist and hips, and firm up the thighs. They lead into the Opposite Arm-Leg Stretch (page 22), then logically into the Figure Eight basic dance movement (page 24). You can do portions of these stretches at odd moments: for example, try pulling the arms up and stretching the rib cage to relax your body while sitting at a desk or watching TV. Contract the buttocks, abdomen, and thighs while you are standing in long checkout lines.

A. *Basic stance:* Place feet slightly apart. Chest up, chin up. Pull arms straight up so they are near your ears, hands turned in. Contract buttocks, abdomen, and backs of legs to tighten and make a strong base for the isolated top movements. Contracted muscles are not "stiff" muscles. Contracted muscles help you control body movements.

B. Stretch up with your right arm, pulling up and out with your wrist. Stretch, hold.

C. Stretch up and out with the left arm, pulling up and out with your wrist. Stretch, hold.

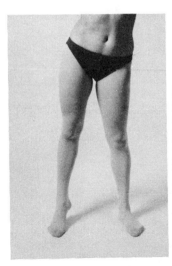

D. *Hip isolation:* Now, hold the rib cage and arms up. Push one heel up from the floor, pushing the hip up without bending your knee. Do not push from side to side; the body should not move. Push up with the rear thigh muscles, then *slowly* put (do not drop) the leg down. When both heels are on the floor, only then push up the other leg. Stretch, hold. Repeat several times.

21

OPPOSITE ARM-LEG STRETCH

Follow the limb stretches with the Opposite Arm-Leg Stretch to gain coordination and make the body more flexible. This stretch, accomplished smoothly to music, is the basis for the body movements used in the slow rhythms and in the advanced Snake Movements. Perform these stretches before a mirror and remember the following:

Coordinate *opposite* limbs.
Pull the rib cage up and out.
Push the hip up with the muscles at the back of the thighs.

Always carry procedures from previous stretches into every new exercise.

As you push up with the right leg, stretch up with the left arm. Stretch, hold; return heel to the floor.

DO the stretches very slowly at first, stretching and holding. Then develop the movement so it flows from one side to the other and becomes stretch, stretch, stretch, stretch, rather than stretch and hold. DO keep your weight on the ball of your foot with your legs straight and knees locked.
DO NOT turn the ankles out or turn out on your little toe.

Stretch and hold, pushing up the left hip and stretching the right arm. Repeat ten times.

FIGURE EIGHT

The Figure Eight is a basic dance movement that adapts to many variations. It involves a side-to-side and back-and-forth hip sway that can be subtle or exaggerated. Carefully learn the breakdown of the movement as an exercise, then work it out smoothly and without a stop at each count. Don't rush this movement; it is most attractive when it is done slowly. *Basic stance:* Weight equally distributed over both legs, feet apart slightly past the hips, buttocks contracted, rib cage and chin up, chest out.

A. Push right hip to right side. DO NOT drop the weight into the hip.

B. Push right heel off floor, pushing the right hip up. The rib cage pulls to the left side.

C. Push right hip straight over to left.

D. Pull right hip down away from the rib cage, right heel down.

When you do the exercise, think of it as four counts: 1) hip out and hold; 2) up and hold; 3) in and over and hold; 4) down and hold, on each side. When you smooth it out, develop it into two movements on each side instead of four: 1) out and up; 2) over and down.

E. Push left hip out.

F. Push left hip up.

G. Push left hip over to right. The rib cage pulls to the right side.

H. Pull left hip down away from the rib cage. Repeat from one side to the other.

25

FIGURE EIGHT VARIATION: BENT KNEES

This Figure Eight Variation involves the same movements as the Figure Eight but with the knees bent and the back slightly arched (like sitting on a horse). This gives your thigh and leg muscles a good stretch. The bent knee position is important to achieve the leverage and control required for hip movements.

Think of the movement as four parts, then smooth out to two as in the basic Figure Eight (page 24).

 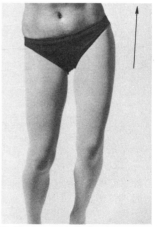

A. *Basic stance:* Knees slightly bent. Push right heel off the floor using the muscles at the outer back of your leg. DO NOT push the knee forward or out to the side. The hip goes *up* into your waistline. Return right heel to the floor.

B. Push up with the left leg, using the same back and side leg muscles as you did on the right side.

C. *The movement (follow the photos clockwise):* Use the same body stretch as the Opposite Arm-Leg Stretch (page 22). With the Figure Eight, push right heel and hip up. Hold.

D. Push off the right toe—pushing the body to the left side and pulling the rib cage out to the left.

E. Pull the right hip down away from the rib cage and stretch up with the right arm. Push left heel and hip off the floor. Hold.

F. Push off the left toe and push the body to the right side, rib cage out to the right.

FIGURE EIGHT VARIATION: UP AND DOWN

Now you are ready to develop the Figure Eight in an up-and-down movement that will be used in all basic and advanced combinations and in striving for a snake effect. The trick is to move the hips in the

A. Push left hip up as you slightly bend down with the right knee.

B. Push the right hip up as the left knee bends a little farther.

C. Push the left hip up again. Bend down still farther with the right knee. Hold.

D. Push up with the right leg while rising slightly on the left knee.

E. Push the left hip up returning to a middle position.

F. Push the right hip up and the body all the way up, left knee still bent slightly. Hold. Repeat from A.

Figure Eight while the knees are bending up and down. With each hip movement, the body descends one beat and sways gently from side to side. Think of the movements as four beats for the descent: 1) down; 2) down; 3) down; 4) hold. For the ascent: 1) up; 2) up; 3) up; 4) hold. *Follow the photos in sequence.*

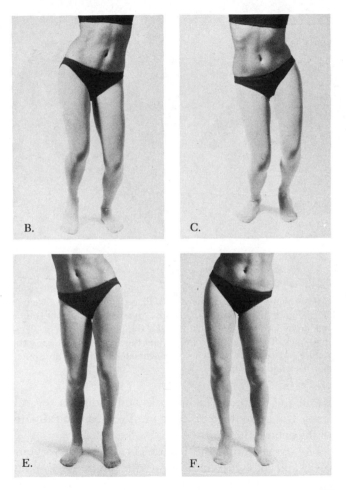

B.

C.

E.

F.

CAMEL WALK: THE PELVIC TILT

The Pelvic Tilt is essential for the Camel Walk movements. It limbers the spine and strengthens the lower torso. It is used extensively during forward-and-backward dance movements.

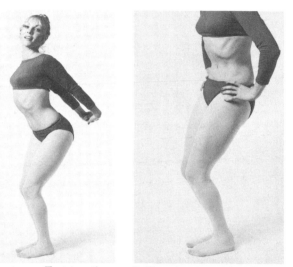

A. *Basic stance:* Feet together, knees slightly bent. Chest out, back arched, the pelvic area tilted back. To straighten your posture, clasp hands behind your back and pull up.

B. Place hands on hips. Keep rib cage up, contract buttocks. Tilt the pelvis up and in. Contract the abdomen, bringing the navel back in toward the spine.

Pull and contract the buttocks and abdomen several times. It may require practice until you can coordinate all the contractions.

The exercise: Do the Pelvic Tilt as you bend your knees and move up and down with the pelvis tipping up and in and back.

A. Place arms out to the side and slightly behind your body.

B. Bring the knees up and pull the chest forward; arch your back.

C. Come back down as you *slowly* contract the buttocks. Tip up the pelvis and bend your knees.

31

CAMEL WALK: FRONT-BACK PELVIC ROLL

The Front-Back Pelvic Roll and the Front-Back Rib Cage Roll (below) are also preparatory to the undulating movement of the Camel Walk. The Pelvic Roll makes the body flexible and strong; it isolates the pelvis from the rib cage and results in a smooth, flowing, front-to-back pelvic movement. Break down each position, then smooth it into a circle with the hips going around, forward, and back, as the knees bend up and down.

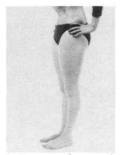

A. Feet together. Tuck in the pelvis. Contract the buttocks.

B. Bend the knees.

D. Lead up and out with the hips and contract back into position A.

C. Arch the back.

A. Contract buttocks, hands on hips.

B. Push back against hips, pull the rib cage forward.

C. Pull rib cage up and out and hold.

D. Push the rib cage down and back, keeping abdomen and buttocks muscles contracted.

CAMEL WALK: FRONT-BACK RIB CAGE ROLL

As the pelvis moves in its front-to-back circle, the rib cage circles from back to front. First, practice the rib cage circle—*holding the pelvis still.* Isolate the roll movements and then smooth them out. This is the object of isolation and control. At the same time you will be tightening up the waist and abdomen. You will put the Pelvic Roll and Rib Cage Roll together after you learn the Camel Walk itself.

THE CAMEL ROCK AND
THE CAMEL WALK

A. *Basic stance:* Separate
the legs slightly with the right
leg behind you. With both
knees straight, stretch the
body *up* and *out*.

With your body flexible and limber from the exercises so far, you are now ready for the Camel Rock
which is done in place by shifting the weight from
the right leg to the left leg and back again. Once you
can gracefully follow the movements, you move forward, and the Camel Walk is accomplished easily and

B. Step back and put your weight on the extended right leg. Bend *down* and contract the abdomen *up*.

C. Arch the back, buttocks out. Push up and forward with the right leg and shift the weight onto the left leg. Move back and forth smoothly from one leg to the other. Think of the movement as: 1) up and out; 2) down and in.

effectively. To move, step forward with the front foot, shift the weight to the front leg. The back leg advances a tiny step and the weight shifts to the back leg. This results in a swaying forward-back movement used in the slow combinations for minimal traveling forward, backward, side to side, in circles, and in arcs.

CAMEL WALK: BACKWARD

To accomplish a backward progression with the Camel Walk, follow the photographs.

A. From the basic stance—back arched, left leg extended out in back, knees straight, body and chest stretched up and out . . .

B. . . . extend the left leg up and in back.

The Camel Rock may be combined with the Backward Camel Walk. Do a rocking movement in the middle position, stepping into a forward-backward rock before taking the full step backward. The movement is B) step; C) back; B) forward; C) back; D) change.

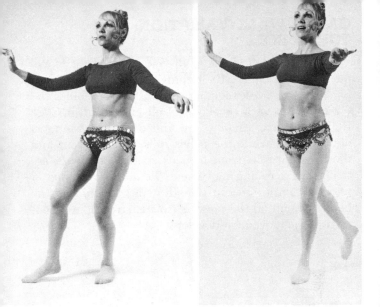

C. Step onto the left leg, shifting the weight off the right leg as you contract the torso in.

D. Stretch the right leg out in back to make the actual step progression.

E. Step back, putting your weight on the right leg. Contract the torso in again to complete one backward step. Continue to move straight backward by changing legs and contracting the torso as you move.

37

CAMEL WALK VARIATION: TORSO ROLL

The Torso Roll is one of the most important movements in the dance. Everything you have learned so far begins to work together. Basically it combines the Camel Walk with the Pelvic Roll and the Rib Cage Roll. The torso stretches up and out, then contracts down and in while the pelvis rolls back to front and the rib cage rolls front to back so that the body actually has a rolling movement. *Follow the photos in sequence* until you can smoothly and *slowly* feel the body roll and all the muscles isolate, stretch, and contract as the movement develops.

A. Pull the rib cage straight forward, legs slightly bent.

B. As the back arches, the pelvis pushes back and the rib cage continues to pull out and up smoothly. The legs straighten. Roll the rib cage around, out, and up.

C. Pull the rib cage straight down and toward the back as the knees begin to bend gradually.

D. Bend the knees, contract abdomen and pelvic area as you pull the rib cage all the way back and down. Return to position A again, straightening the legs.

CAMEL WALK VARIATION: SIDE TO SIDE

This variation of the Camel Walk is a versatile step used for moving forward and from side to side. Think

A. Left leg stretched out in back. Step slightly to the right side and forward with the weight on the right leg.

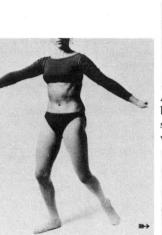

B. Contract the torso as you bend the knees and pivot on the right leg.

C. Turn to the left, lift the right heel slightly, and pivot on the ball of the left foot.

of the movement as 1) up and out; 2) straight in and
down; 3) pivot; 4) hold. Then stretch up and out to
the other side, contract straight down and in, and
pivot. *Follow the photos counterclockwise.*

F. Then step up and out,
returning to position A. As you
pivot from side to side, you can
do the Camel Rock between
positions A to F and A to B,
then on to C.

E. Contract the torso, bend the
knees slightly, pivot, and
turn to the right into
position F.

D. Stretch up and out with the
weight on the left leg.

41

CHAPTER 3

SHIMMIES AND OTHER
HIP MOVEMENTS

The quick, short, side-to-side, back-to-front hip movements that seem to start all of you jiggling, that flutter the fringe and frenzy the coins, also make the flesh quiver whether you're the dancer or the observer. Are these eye-boggling movements as difficult as they appear? Of course not. Actually, they require less effort than many other movements, and a dancer may do an easy shimmy while she catches her breath from the more exerting portions of the dance.

To do the shimmy, first isolate the hip movement as a shake, then make it shorter and faster, and, voilà, you are almost motorized.

Shimmies may cause a pain in the upper abdomen from the forced contraction of muscles that never have been used this way. As you condition the muscles, the pain will subside—along with a lot of excess flab from around your middle.

Shakes and shimmies are performed to different tempos during any and all portions of the music. Practice them to music with an accented drumbeat but only *after* you have loosened up with the basic exercises in chapter 2. To accentuate the effect of the shimmy, now is the time to don that coin belt and work it into its frantic wiggling and jiggling. The noisier it is, the better you are!

Basic stance for all hip movements: Knees bent, back slightly arched, chest up, head held high with the neck straight —as though someone is pulling your head off the shoulders from the neck. Elbows up, arms extended to the side at about shoulder and bust level.

DO NOT drop the weight into the hips and waist.
DO NOT swing the hips back and forth or bump them.
DO NOT think of the hip movement as coming from the buttocks; it comes from the top of the hipbone.

FORWARD-BACKWARD HIP SHAKE

A free-swinging isolated hip movement requires a slight bending of the knees. *Only* for the breakdown

A. For the Forward-Back Hip Shake exercise, stand with the feet apart and slightly behind the hips; buttocks contracted, rib cage up out of waistline.

and exercise, below, are the knees straight. Once you feel the movement, *then* bend the knees, and you are in condition for the various shakes and shimmies that follow.

 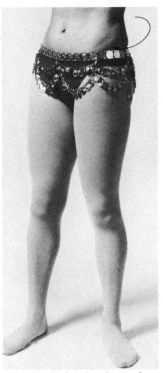

B. Twist the right hip forward as far as you can, keeping both feet flat on the floor and the legs straight. (Extend the arms out at the sides about chest level.) This is a one-two beat with the accent on each forward movement.

C. Twist the left hip forward as far as you can. Repeat until you can twist each hip forward and back comfortably and smoothly. As the hips move forward and back with more speed, the twists become smaller, and the shake becomes a shimmy.

SIDE TO SIDE AND UP AND DOWN

As the hips shimmy, the body can move in various directions. Practice this side-to-side and up-and-down

A. Step out to the side with your left leg.

F. Shift the weight to the right leg and pivot on the ball of the right foot. Read the photos as D E F; F E D.

movement *following the photos clockwise.* Then, when you have the movement worked out, do the Forward-Backward Hip Shake until you can make it faster and smaller so that you are shimmying while you are moving from side to side and up and down.

B. Bend both knees, but put your weight only on the left leg.

C. Pivot on the ball of the left foot.

E. Turn to the center, again bending both knees a little lower than D.

D. Lean back and come up slightly.

SIDE HIP THRUST

The side-to-side thrusting motion of the Side Hip Thrust offers variety, dimension, and softness to the dance and enables you to move in various directions. It firms the waist, buttocks, and thighs. Remember to hold the body tight.

A. Weight on the right leg.

B. Thrust the right hip forward.

C. Thrust the right hip all the way back, weight still on the right leg.

D. Thrust the right hip forward again.

E. Change the weight to the left leg.

F. Thrust the left hip forward.

G. Thrust the left hip back.

H. Thrust the left hip forward again. Repeat from A.

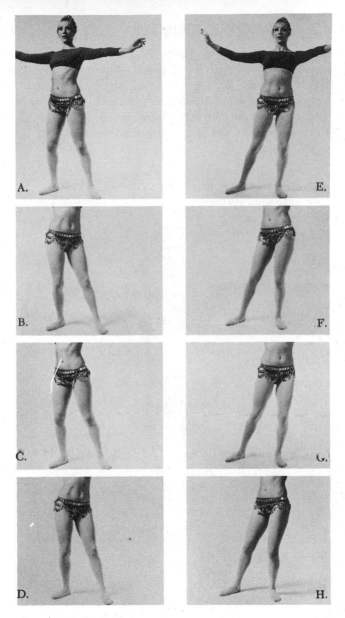

49

UP-AND-DOWN SHIMMY

In the first shimmy (page 44), the hips moved forward and back. In the Up-and-Down Shimmy, the knees bend up and down slowly as the hips shimmy up and down more rapidly. Begin the hips moving up and down, slowly at first, then pick up speed as you descend and ascend to a sharp one-two drumbeat.

A. Feet together flat on floor, arms extended. Push the right hip *up*.

B. Push the left hip up.

C. Push the right hip up.

D. Then straighten the legs and continue the Up-and-Down Shimmy as you bend and straighten the knees to descend and ascend slightly. For an advanced movement, the shimmy is done up and down and back and forth simultaneously. Some people can do this automatically. If you can do both, don't worry about shimmying in one direction only.

51

THIGH SHIMMY

The Thigh Shimmy gives you almost the same feeling as the Scooting Shimmy. The difference is that the Scooting Shimmy is done on your toes and you are moving forward. For the Thigh Shimmy, you are flat on your feet and standing in one place.

Feet flat, body position with the buttocks contracted; move only the thighs back and forward very rapidly and alternately. In the advanced movements, the Thigh Shimmy can be used with Traveling Steps, Hip Circles, and others.

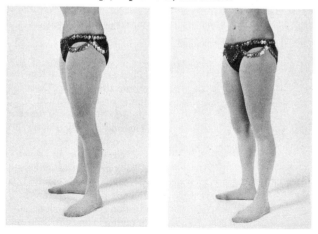

SCOOTING SHIMMY

The Scooting Shimmy is a forward-moving step that makes all your flesh feel like it is shaking and tingling. It is used to end the very fast, happy parts of the dance. The movement is derived from the ethnic Turkish style of belly dancing. Keep the body tight.

Chin and rib cage up, chest forward, arms back and slightly arched, knees bent. Stand on your toes and take very small, forward scooting steps with the thighs moving quickly backward and forward alternately.

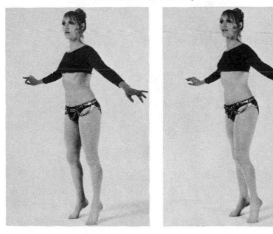

HIP DROP

The Hip Drop occurs between the knee and the waistline and results from keeping the heel off the floor and simultaneously lifting and dropping the hip.

A. Legs straight, push the left heel up from the floor; this pushes the left hip up (not out).

B. Keep the left heel off the floor and strongly arch the left foot. Bend the left knee.

A and B give you the position. C and D are the movement. It is done to medium-fast and fast tempos and can be combined with the Up-and-Down Shimmy (page 50) and the Front-Back Hip Drop (page 144).

C. Bend the right knee slightly, still keeping the left heel off the floor, and push the left hip up.

D. Pull the left hip down away from the rib cage with the heel still raised from the floor and the foot arched. The heel must be raised to give the leg leverage to move the hip only; otherwise the whole body drops. Repeat on the right side. Then alternate left to right, or do two or three on one side and then alternate.

HIP DROP ROTATION

The Hip Drop Rotation leads into advanced movements—not necessarily faster movements. Often, the more complex a movement, the more beautiful and

A. Push the left hip up. (Heel up and foot arched.)

D. Push the left hip up.

E. Push the left heel down and push the right hip up.

sensual it appears when it is performed slowly. The Hip Drop on pages 54-55 now twists and rotates to the front and alternates from the left to the right hip. Keep the rib cage up.

B. Turn the left hip forward.

C. Drop the left hip down in front.

F. Turn the right hip forward . . .

G. . . . and drop the right hip down away from the rib cage. Repeat from A.

SIDE-TO-SIDE HIP DROP

Another Hip Drop, that can be used for variation, moves from side to side. *Follow the photos clockwise.*

A. Begin with this position. Push the *left* heel off the floor and drop the *left* hip down.

E. Step down with right foot and drop the right hip. Then push the right foot off the floor. Lead with the right hip and step over onto the right leg and return to A. Reverse and *follow the photos counterclockwise. Start over again clockwise.*

B. Push the left foot up off the floor and the left hip up.

C. Lead to the left with the left hip and take a small step to the left side . . .

D. . . . onto the left foot. Then lift the right hip up.

HIP LIFT

The Hip Lift is another seductive hip movement that is also a beneficial exercise. The hips are isolated, and the movement is only from the waist down. Each

A. Lift the right leg up and slightly out to the side.

foot comes off the floor on alternate counts as the hip is lifted up and slightly to the side, away from the body. One hip comes off the floor on each count, so it is 1) lift; 2) lift. When it is done rapidly it can be 1) lift; 2) lift; 3) lift; 4) hold. In the advanced movements, this becomes a Traveling Step.

B. Lift the left leg up and slightly out to the side.

HIP CIRCLE

The Hip Circle pulls the hips around in one direction and the rib cage in the other. What a way to reduce the waistline and firm the upper thighs! During the dance, the circle is large in the slow tempos and minimized in the faster sections. *Follow the photos counterclockwise* about five times. Then reverse the circle.

A. Arms out to the side, feet apart. Thrust the pelvis forward, rib cage back.

B. Push the right hip to the right side, bend the right knee slightly, and stretch the left leg out until you feel a stretching on the inside of the right thigh.

D. Push the left hip out to the left side, left knee bent, and right leg stretched out straight so you feel a pull and stretch in the right inner thigh.

C. Push the pelvis backward and bend the chest slightly forward. Now the legs are straight, arms at shoulder level, and chin up.

CHAPTER 4

ARM MOVEMENTS

The provocative hip movements hold great fascination for belly dance aficionados. The experienced dancer, however, is aware of the magic of gracefully flowing arms. The arms carry the fluidity of the dance from the toes to the fingertips, and they express the entire range of emotions that are ingrained in Middle Eastern melodies. One's hip movements may be fantastic, but if the arms are poorly coordinated, the whole dance will suffer.

What is the secret to snaring the snakelike, magnetizing arm movements that complement the undulating torso? You learn to isolate the shoulders, elbows, wrists, hands, and finger muscles, one at a time, and then to smooth out the positions. Such esoteric isolations appear to defy what nature wanted the arms to do, and the movements may seem awkward and difficult at first.

The following exercises should be practiced in front of your mirror. (You can use them to relieve sore shoulders that are strained from desk work, bending, carrying, and long-distance driving.) Do them slowly, carefully, patiently. DO NOT expect to accomplish all of them at once.

Always be conscious of the position of your arms. They are held at chest and shoulder level. Never are they forgotten and allowed to hang loosely at the hips, to flap around in space, nor should your hands stroke the air as though you are swimming. Neither must they be held so stiff that the dance appears wooden. Arm and hand movements must be soft and unobtrusive, yet they must whisper thousands of unspoken words to your audience.

And what an expressive asset the hands can become —down to the tiniest curve of your little finger. Often they will slowly scribe a circle through several bars of a medium-slow, haunting melody. The body is quiescent. The spotlight plays only on the fingers and hands curling, curving, and casting their magical mood with practiced, beautiful gestures.

You'll discover, too, how to play the *zills,* or finger cymbals, those tiny bronze clappers that create a distinctive ring and beat for the belly dancer.

Coordinating all these previously unused muscles takes effort and practice, but the results are staggering. You'll increase your potential for performing the dance well. You will also exercise muscles that will improve your posture and your walk. The exercises will reduce and firm flab in the upper arm; they will minimize or eliminate a dowager's hump. They have brought relief to arthritis and rheumatism sufferers, and they have restored elasticity and muscle tone to many who have had surgery in the upper torso. If a medical problem exists, always consult your physician before you attempt the exercises.

POSITION FOR ARM MOVEMENTS

Always begin the arm movements from a straight, tall posture with the head up, the rib cage pulled out of the waistline, and the buttocks tucked under. Extend arms to the sides at bust or shoulder level. Loosen up the arms by rotating them back and forth, then bending the elbows and bringing the hands to the chest and out again. Now you are ready for the arm isolation positions.

Shoulder Isolation: Turn the right shoulder forward by twisting it slightly. DO NOT lift the shoulder toward your ear or body. Only twist it forward, then back. Slowly. With concentration.

Shoulder-Elbow Isolation: Turn the left shoulder forward and then the elbow up toward the ceiling with the wrist bent and the hand straight out, as shown. Keep your arms at the sides, not in front or in back of your body. If you have trouble keeping the hand straight, practice by placing the hand flat on a table and pulling the shoulder forward and the elbow up.

Repeat each isolation several times with each arm, then alternate the arms so they work into a smooth, sinuous snakelike movement.

BACKWARD ARM CIRCLE

After practicing the Shoulder-Elbow Isolation, you will begin to make a backward circle with the arm. Continue the movement from the position of the Shoulder-Elbow Isolation (previous page). Imagine

B. Lead up with the right elbow, and lift the whole arm straight up.

A. With the right shoulder forward, move the right arm slightly forward with the wrist out.

you have a small ball under your armpit that prevents you from dropping your arm next to your body. Make the movements slow, definite, and controlled. DO NOT close up the armpit. DO NOT let the hands hang or droop; always be aware of what they are doing. Repeat with opposite arms, then alternate the arms.

C. Still leading with the elbow, bring the arm straight back at shoulder level.

D. Now lead the arm down with the elbow first; the shoulder will turn back. Open the hand on the way down. Reverse arms and repeat from A.

Think of turning the shoulder in and the arm forward and count: 1) start the backward circle, turn the shoulder in; 2) elbow up with wrist bent; 3) elbow back; and 4) arm slowly down.

HAND AND FINGER POSITIONS

For a snakelike movement, the hands must follow through and be as controlled as the arms. As you lead up and out with the wrist and back of the hand for the Backward Arm Circle (pages 68-69), the fingers are straight down. As the hand comes up, it performs a circle of its own. DO NOT move the hands as though you are swimming. DO NOT move both arms simultaneously: when one is up, the other is down.

A. In the basic arm position, place the fingers straight down, arch the wrist strongly, turn the shoulder in and the elbow up.

B. Lead out and up with the wrist, keeping the fingers straight.

C. As you lift the arm and near the top, the elbow begins to come down and the fingers begin to bend.

D. As the elbow comes down, the hand continues up a little more and begins to make its circle.

All arm movements begin with the shoulder—then the elbow, wrist, and hand. If you are moving only your elbows and wrists, you are doing it incorrectly.

These arm movements may be done during slow musical tempos while the body is relatively quiet or as you ascend and descend. Often the hand movements alone are the center of attention during the floor movements.

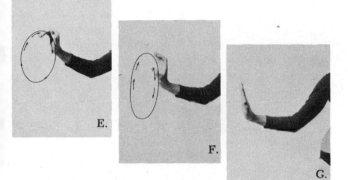

E. The hand begins to drop down and the fingers arch gracefully away from the palm.

F. The arm continues its descent while the hand finishes scribing the circle and the fingers open slightly.

G. When the arm reaches the bottom point at waist level, the hand should be open and up, the fingers together and straight. Repeat from A. Practice with each hand, then alternate.

SIDE-TO-SIDE ARM MOVEMENTS

So far, you have learned how to isolate the arm muscles, to move the arms up and down and in a backward circle. Now use the same isolations and move the arms from side to side as you do the Figure Eight body movement (page 24). This is a fluid, graceful step that begins slowly, builds up to a medium-fast pace, and returns to a slow, taunting tempo.

The photos exaggerate the positions slightly. With practice, you will be able to fluidly move from one side to the other.

A. When the body sways to the right side, the arm leads out to the right. Remember, shoulder forward first, then elbow, wrist, hand.

B. When the body sways to the left side, the elbow comes down and pulls in, and the hand opens. The hand scribes the circle shown on the previous page.

When you combine the Side-to-Side Arm Movements with the Figure Eight, remember that opposite arms and legs are used.

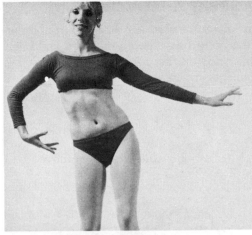

C. Push up with the left hip,
the body and rib cage sway
to the right, and the right arm
leads out to the right side.

D. When you push the right
hip up, the body and rib cage
sway to the left, and the left
arm leads out to the left side.

FRONT-BACK ARM MOVEMENT

As the arms move forward and back in an undulating motion, the body sways gently forward and back. The concentration is on the upper torso; no other hip or body movements are combined.

A. Stand in the position shown, keeping the left foot forward. Begin with the left arm, while the right arm holds its position waiting for its turn. Lead with the shoulder first, following with the arched elbow and the back of the wrist. Keep arms at shoulder or bust level and never lower than the waist. The hand does a backward circle. DO NOT use a swimming stroke!

B. When the right arm leads out, shoulder first, the left arm pulls back, shoulder first.

C. As one arm goes up and the other moves down, the hands cross at about chest level and should be held close to one another.

FINGER CYMBALS (ZILLS)

Finger cymbals are also called by the Arabic term, *zills*, or the Turkish, *sagats*. They echo the rhythm of the drum, and they provide a melodious nuance at the dancer's discretion. They may be worn and used during selected parts of the dance or throughout the performance. Their cadence varies, sometimes producing a rapid-fire staccato ring where one sound blends into another, sometimes clanged slowly so that each clear ring lingers in the air.

Cymbals are usually made of bronze or brass, four to a set, and are available in different weights from dance suppliers, Greek gift shops, and the firm listed in the Supply Sources. Always fit a new set of cymbals tightly to your fingers by pinning or sewing in a piece of strong elastic; they must never fly into the audience or at the band.

Before working with the cymbals, listen carefully for the drumbeats in any record and practice them with your fingers. The drum has two sounds, usually a bass beat which is heavier and more solid than the shorter, higher rhythms. Think of the solid, longer bass beat as Ā and the shorter beats as TEK (see chapter 10).

Use the left hand to beat the Ā, the bass beat.
Use the right hand for the TEK.

Cymbals are sometimes removed before performing floor positions so they don't hamper the snake hand movements. When you put them on again, pick them up with graceful arm motions and do any Shimmy with your back to the audience. As you slip the cymbals back on, never stop dancing entirely.

Cymbals are positioned on the thumb and middle finger between the knuckle and fingernail, or just at the bottom of the nail. Turn them so they hit one another squarely.

Always keep elbows up while practicing and playing the cymbals. Do not let the arms drop. The left hand hits the bass A beat.

Bring the finger down to the thumb.

As you play the cymbals, the hands can be in any of the arm movements shown, or they may be positioned over your head with one arm higher than the other. The wrists should be down.

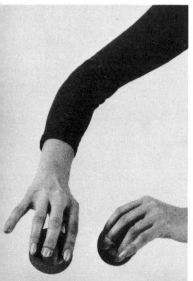

When very rapid beats are desired, the second and fourth fingers can be placed on the cymbal for more control. The rapid beat is a *one and one and one and one* (TEK-TEK-TEK-TEK) and requires that the fingers hold the cymbals closer together than in the basic Ā-TEK-TEK beat.

For another fast variation, place the right-hand cymbals inside those on the left hand. Swing the right hand within the left hand so that the right-hand pair of cymbals actually hits the left-hand pair of open cymbals, one on each side of the left hand. The result is a very fast *ring*.

Another effective sound variation during slower rhythms is accomplished by hitting the cymbals sideways, one off the other. They are hit with a sideward, sliding motion which produces a rolling *ring* rather than a sharp *clang*.

SHOULDER SHIMMY

The Shoulder Shimmy is one possible conclusion for the arm movements. It takes advantage of the shoulder muscles you have learned to isolate. The shoulders move forward and back very subtly, one shoulder and then the other. The movement becomes a shimmy as the shoulders move in a smaller area and at a faster speed. This should not be an exaggerated movement where the bosom shakes; it is loveliest when it is subtle and suggestive, not coarse. The Shoulder Shimmy can be done while the body sways down and back, up and forward, as shown at right. Tighten up the chest and arm muscles and keep the arms almost at bust level.

HEAD SLIDE

The Head Slide is reminiscent of Egyptian and Balinese dances and probably was borrowed from these sources and used by Middle Easterners. It is based on isolating the head to move independently of

A. To practice the Head Slide, push the hands tightly together under your chin; keep the elbows up to prevent the shoulders from moving.

the shoulders. It may be incorporated into the dance when you are in a kneeling or standing position, or when you peek seductively over the edge of a taut and tauntingly held veil. The Head Slide is accompanied by a subtle drumbeat in a *one-two-three, hold* tempo.

B. Use the ear and jaw as a point of concentration and think of gliding or pulling with the ear and jaw to the right side. DO NOT tip your head.

C. Pull the left ear and jaw to the left side. DO NOT tip the head or shoulders. Reverse sides and repeat several times.

CHAPTER 5

VEIL MOVEMENTS

A filmy veil floating gracefully about a whirling dancer is a special, ethereal vision. Creating this effect is easy when you follow the movements illustrated. Use the veil imaginatively. Be mysterious and aloof as you peek mystically over an edge. Later, swing the veil aside with brazen abandonment and begin another part of the dance.

The first practice veil should be lightweight chiffon or nylon, hemmed and without any edge trimming. The average veil is about 2½ yards long and 48 to 54 inches wide. Short girls may find a 2-yard length easier to handle.

The costume veil can be made of a heavier fabric and may be trimmed with beads, lightweight coins, or sequined edging. Sari cloth and hand-painted chiffons can be effective. The trim should never make the veil so heavy that the flowing movement is hampered.

The dancer usually enters with her veil beautifully draped and lightly tucked into her hip band at the back and under a bra strap in the front—to give a "covered up" look. After performing several movements with the veil tucked in, she untucks it and twirls until she gracefully drops it behind her.

A veil is not essential; many dancers enter with a portion of their skirt tucked into their bra. A sleeveless harem coat may be designed. But whatever you use, the veil movements are exceptionally good for limbering the upper torso because you pull the arms out and around while you stretch from the waist.

VEIL SWIRL

For the Veil Swirl, the veil is swirled around your body as you remain in a frontal position. Lean slightly

A. Stand with your feet apart, arms outstretched and up, the veil held between the thumb and index finger so the fabric is taut along the top.

B. Hold arms out away from your body. Pull both arms to the right side. Bend slightly to the right.

C. Lead with the left hand and pull the veil out . . .

in the direction you pull the veil and bend from your waist. DO NOT stand ramrod straight and move only your arms, or the veil will land on your head. *Follow the photos counterclockwise.*

F. Pull the right hand around and out over your head and to the back. Follow through with the right hand and back to position A. Repeat until you can do the movement smoothly.

E. Continue the movement by pulling the veil to your left. The left hand moves down and the right hand moves up.

D. . . . and around to the front.

87

FIGURE EIGHT VEIL

Swirling the veil in a Figure Eight movement is an attractive variation for the veil portion of the dance. Actually, you can move the veil any way you like as long as it looks graceful and you have fun.

Stand with the feet slightly apart. Shift your body gracefully and smoothly from one side to the other as you move your rib cage and arms.

To complete any of the veil movements, bring your hands together in back, still holding the veil. Grasp the veil in one hand, bring it up over your head, twirl it two or three times, gather it, and toss it toward the band. On a large stage, toss it away from your dancing area and let it float to the floor.

Always lead with the hand in the direction you are going. The left hand pulls up to the left as the body moves to the left, and vice versa.

VEIL AND BODY TWIRL

For the Veil and Body Twirl, both you and the veil twirl in a circle. *Follow the photos counterclockwise.*

A. Begin with the veil behind you, your back to the audience.

B. Turn to your left and, as you turn, pull the veil around in front of you.

C. Cross your arms and bend forward as you . . .

F. . . . up in back. You can twirl around with your back to the audience and repeat the movement or remain in the frontal position and do either the Veil Swirl (page 86) or the Figure Eight Veil (page 88).

E. Come up with the body and swirl the veil up around and . . .

D. . . . bring the veil down low in front and then up and around to the back.

SIDE-TO-SIDE VEIL

This lovely Side-to-Side Veil movement can be done as you walk forward and pivot. Pull the veil around from one side to the other as you arch your body and extend the right leg out to the side. Take three small steps forward and pivot, and do the same movement on left side. Think of it as a *one, two, three, turn* movement. As you turn from side to side, pull the veil around as in the Veil Swirl (pages 86-87).

HAREM VEIL

The Harem Veil is a delightful, enticing veil position that can serve as a pause to the swirling veil variations. Hold the veil between the first and second fingers and cover the arms. Bring the hands up and frame the face while you do the Head Slide (page 82); to accentuate the action, focus your eyes in the same direction the head is moving.

The floor exercises both prepare
you for and become the dance
movements.

CHAPTER 6

EXERCISES THAT LEAD TO GREATER THINGS

Movements accomplished while the dancer is down on the floor are intriguing and exciting, and they are a major portion of Middle Eastern dancing. The body undulates gracefully backward, forward, and in sinuous rolls that may be accompanied by snaky arms, Shoulder Shimmies, Abdominal Flutters, and a variety of mesmerizing sways.

Performing these movements fluidly and with apparent ease requires advance work so that you have optimum control of the muscles in your torso, thighs, chest, head, shoulders, and arms. The floor exercises, designed to lead you into the actual floor movements in chapter 7, will slim, stretch, and limber your body in a different way.

Always preface the floor exercises with the warm-up stretches in chapter 2. Then begin with the first sitting exercise in this chapter and follow through as the exercises are presented—but not all at once. Attempt one at a time and deliberately plan to progress slowly. After you feel limbered, try the beginning positions for one or two of the following exercises until you are stretched sufficiently to go on. Your progress will depend on how often you exercise as well as on your determination and ability.

B. Keep your back straight and lead forward with your chest. Keep your chin up and your knees extended out as far as possible. Stretch—stretch forward as far as you can.

A. Place feet together, knees out to sides, hands on toes. Pull back against the feet. Pull your chest up, out, and forward between the arms. You should feel your spine straighten.

C. Contract your abdomen and slowly lower your chin to your chest.

D. Pull the torso back . . .

E. . . . and follow through by pulling the chest up, out, and forward through the arms again. Repeat at least five times.

97

A. Another excellent body
stretch begins from the above
position. Straighten your spine,
keep your weight in your chest,
abdomen in, and chin up. Do
this stretch slowly, two or more
times on each side. Don't rush
it. It's perfect for relaxing,
firming, and limbering you
from head to toe.

B. Stretch the chest over the left leg and hold the position for five long, slow counts. Do not bounce, just hold.

C. Slowly drop the head to the knee and hold for five more counts.

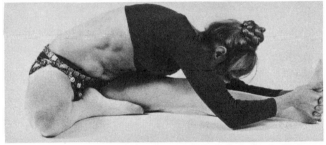

D. Turn to the left side with the right arm over your ear— not out in front of your face. Hold for ten slow counts. You'll feel the stretch all along the side of your body. Repeat over the other leg.

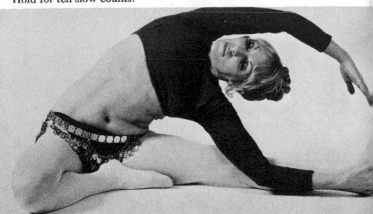

A. This marvelous stretch-exercise will reduce waist and thighs. Assume the position shown. Sit as straight as possible and bring your clasped hands up in back to force the chest out.

B. With your chest forward and back straight, place your hands on your legs, as shown.

C., D. Then pull down,
leading with your chest. Slowly
swing from side to side about
ten times.

TO GREATER THINGS #4

In this exercise, the body is actually making a forward rolling motion. Follow the rolling through very slowly, always contracting the abdomen as you come up. Concentrate on each position of the body in turn as it progresses. Do not rush.

A. Begin in this position with the abdomen tight and the weight pulled up into the chest.

B. Stretch forward, leading with the chest. Chin up.

E. The head is the last part to come up. Reverse legs and repeat from position A.

D. Slowly pull up with the back of your shoulders and roll out of the contraction.

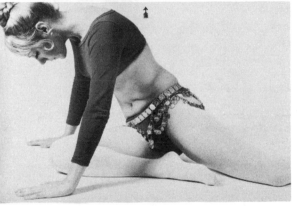

C. Drop your head, contract your abdomen.

103

A. If you can sit between your feet with your buttocks on the floor, assume this position for the next stretch.

B. If you cannot place your buttocks all the way down, lean back on your hands, bringing your hips down toward the floor as far as you can.

C. Slowly push the hips
forward and the chest up and
out. Return to the original
position and stretch up again
as many times as necessary
until you feel you are
"stretched out."

TO GREATER THINGS #6

Begin with A and *follow the position clockwise.*

C. Bring your hands out to your sides.

B. Slide your hands toward your knees and lower your head to the floor.

A. When you feel sufficiently "stretched out" from the previous exercise, continue with this series and repeat about three times. Raise your body, with your weight in your chest. Keep the whole body tight. Place your hands on your heels.

D. Lower the back of your shoulders to the floor and continue sliding your hands out to the sides. Keep your hips up off the floor.

E. Lower the hips slowly to the floor, always keeping the body tight.

F. To get up, push against the floor with the left arm, pull up and over across the chest with the right arm until the shoulders come up. You can also get up by rolling the chest to a sitting position. This exercise is the basis for the advanced dance movements.

A. This floor roll to one side is an exercise that becomes an advanced Serpentine Roll performed with both feet beneath the body. Begin from the position shown, your right foot close to your bent left knee. Your right hip is on the floor.

B Slide the right hand out to the back and lower your body.

C. Roll the left shoulder onto the floor, bringing the left hand over and around your head. Arm and head are on the floor.

D. Extend the left hand onto the floor, both arms outstretched.

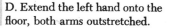

H. Keep your back straight
and your chest over your right
knee and come up to a
sitting position.

↑

G. Continue pulling
the left arm around in front
of your body.

↑

F. Rolling on the right shoulder,
swing the left arm over your
head and gracefully pull it
out to the right arm.

↑

E. Begin the roll by pushing
against the right hand and
lifting the left shoulder and arm.

CHAPTER 7

FLOOR MOVEMENTS

Watching the artful belly dancer gracefully twist into tortuous positions, her hands snaking above her head and her hips shimmying to the doleful sounds of the oud, is a breathtaking experience. You can do it, too, after you've strengthened your body with the exercises in the previous chapter. You'll be astonished at how readily you can accomplish the gravity-defying movements that will make your audience gasp and applaud for more.

Once you have mastered the following breakdown of the Floor Descent and the Ascent, whatever you do can be sheer fun, joy, and personal improvisation. You can call into full play all you have learned, combining undulating Hip Lifts, shimmies, and circles while on your knees. You can lean back and concentrate on tormentingly teasing hand movements that follow the chant of the slow, sad, emotion-filled music. You may appear as though in a trance while your arms and hands spiral, twist, and snake. When you have established the mood, you can slowly rise and slither into Serpentine Rolls and other slow positions as though you are in the eye of a storm that promises exciting, frenzied developments.

Never rush these beautiful movements. Change their pace as the music and interest demand. This is your opportunity to express the way you feel, to be as dramatic, as sultry, and as sensual as you dare.

*Basic stance for the floor
descent:* Left leg straight and
foot pointed slightly left for
balance, right leg extended
in back, arms held out in back.
Your head is held high and
your torso is forward with the
weight held up in the chest.

111

A. Begin from the basic stance. Bend the right knee, slide the right leg farther down in back, and bend the left knee. Your chest must be pulled out over your left knee, and the right foot must be turned out for balance.

B. Slide the right leg down slowly until the knee is on the floor, keeping all your weight over the left foot and your chest over the left knee.

FLOOR DESCENT WITH A BODY ROLL

The transition from a stance down to the floor and back again requires a graceful descent and ascent. After you have followed each step of this movement, carefully smooth it out into one lovely motion. Once you are beautifully ensconced, you are free to improvise with any of the other floor movements described, in any sequence you like. Or you can use the movements in the order presented as a basic combination and then build on it.

C. Slowly, pull the left arm and the body straight up.

D. Extend the left leg straight out to the back.

E. With the chest over the right knee, bring your right hand behind you to the floor and . . .

113

F. . . . slide down all the way,
placing your right hip on the
floor and using your right
hand for balance and support.

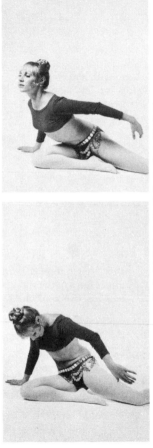

G., H. At this point, perform the forward body roll—"To Greater Things #4" (chapter 6) —as a smooth, follow-through transition into the Torso Circle (following) or into another movement. Lead down with the chest and roll up slowly as you contract the torso and carry the flow through with your arms. When the body is forward, the arms are to the back. As the body begins to roll up and back, the left arm moves forward.

This Floor Descent may be accomplished on either the right or left side.

TORSO CIRCLE

Begin with A and *follow the positions clockwise.*

C. Lead with and emphasize the forward left shoulder movement.

B. . . . begin to move your upper torso to the right, leading with your chest.

A. The Torso Circle can be performed following the forward body roll. Keep the right hip on the floor throughout. Begin in this position and, keeping your back straight . . .

D. Bring the left arm around to the front and, as it circles forward and around to the back, do continuous snake arm movements.

E. Continue to move your torso around in a circle, pushing up from the floor with the right arm and all the time doing circles with the left hand.

F. Pull up and forward, leading with the chest up. Swing your left arm back and your chest forward. Continue on to A and repeat. You might use four Torso Circles in a dance combination. Perform them very slowly with strong, controlled, and deliberate movement during the slow musical tempos.

117

B. Push the torso up, lean on the right arm, and strongly lead up with the chest and left arm.

A. From the basic floor position shown, begin to lead the torso up by raising the left arm.

TORSO CIRCLE VARIATION

In the first Torso Circle, the torso moved around to the right (it may also be performed on the left side). In this variation, the torso moves up and around as you rise up on your knees.

C. Bring the left arm over the head. Stretch and *hold* for at least one count. Gracefully and slowly bring the left arm down and forward in front of your face.

D. Contract the torso and slowly bring the hips to the floor.

E. With your chest over your right knee, lead the left hand around and out in front as you return up to position A. Repeat this circle three or four times during a dance combination.

SNAKE MOVEMENTS: THE SITTING COBRA

The Sitting Cobra, which is fun to do and exciting to watch, is often used as a transition from the slow circles and rolls into the shimmying movements performed in the floor positions.

A. With your knees and feet together, keep your back straight, arms near your ears, and weight up in the chest.

B. The right hip leads up and out to the right side. Feel that you are pulling your hip out and down away from your rib cage.

C. Push the hips forward and then up to the center.

D. The left hip leads out to the right side, pulling down away from the body. Then reverse; C, B, A.

The Sitting Cobra may be performed in the up-and-down side-to-side positions as shown. It may be also smoothed out into a circle that moves to the side, hips up in front, to the other side, then down in back to the heels, and up.

A. Pull the rib cage to the left side. The left shoulder is turned slightly in and up.

SNAKE VARIATION

A sinuous variation of the Sitting Cobra also begins from the kneeling position. The arms and the rib cage follow through with the hip movement. Use this variation about four times during the slow music with a series of four drumbeats: *one-two-three, hold*.

B. You begin to descend by sliding the knees slightly apart and pulling to the right side with the right shoulder and rib cage. Be sure your back is flat and your rib cage is out over your knees.

C. Pull to the left with the left shoulder and rib cage as you continue the movement farther downward, and extend the body to the left. To go up, reverse the positions in a snakelike movement. Then reverse; B, A.

A. Tighten the buttocks and
keep the hips pulled forward.
Extend your arms out to the
side as you bend backward.
As you descend with the music,
keep the arms and hands
slowly snaking.

THE SERPENTINE ROLL

The exotic Serpentine Roll is usually performed
slowly to a soft drum roll. The music may be sus-
pended entirely, as the audience breathlessly wonders
if you'll make it all the way down. The exercise "To
Greater Things #7" (chapter 6) will have strengthened your thighs so that you can descend with beautiful control. You roll gently on the floor and bring yourself back up to a sitting position as effortlessly as
though you have been doing it all your life. At least
that's the way the practiced movement should appear.

B. Lower the shoulders to the
floor and, if you can, hold
and snake the arms a few times.

C. This is the beginning of
the floor roll. Now is the time
to use the arm movement with
the snakelike *hand* undulations
over your head. Then begin
to come up: push against the
left hand and pull the right
shoulder up and over as you . . .

D. . . . continue to push off the
floor with the left hand and . . .

E. . . . pull around in front with
the right shoulder and arm . . .

F. . . . keeping the chest over
the thighs and the back straight.

G. Continue around,
leading with the right shoulder
and right arm.

H. Place the right arm on the
floor and slide out to repeat
another roll. You might
perform the Serpentine Roll
two or more times during the
floor movements and then
return to a kneeling position
and to other snake movements
and variations.

BODY LIFT

Add the Body Lift to the floor movements as a transition or as a basis for body rolls and shimmies while you are on your knees. Begin from A and *follow the photos clockwise.* A and B may be used as warm-up stretch exercises.

C. Bend the left knee and bring it next to the right knee.

B. Push the hips and body up from the floor and stretch the left side. Hold this position for four counts.

A. Sit on your right hip with the right hand eighteen to twenty-four inches away from the body, depending upon the length of your arms. Stretch the left leg out to the side with the right foot under the left thigh. Stretch the left arm out and up next to your ear.

D. Bring your torso up, weight over your feet.

E. Lean to the left, place the left arm on the floor, and raise the right arm.

F. Push the hips up as you stretch the right leg out to the side and hold. When you repeat, reverse and *follow the photos counterclockwise* from F to A.

SHIMMY ON YOUR KNEES

The floor movements are so spectacular that adding other movements along with them is like icing on the cake. One beautiful standby to perform in every situation is a shimmy. When you are on your knees, the shimmy is accomplished by twisting from the waist. First practice the exercise, below, and then lean back and do the movement with your shoulders on the floor.

A. *The exercise:* Sit between your feet and lean back on your arms. Push the hips off the floor and twist the left hip up and forward sharply.

B. Twist the right hip up and forward sharply; the left hip moves back. Repeat this hip twist in this position until you can do it smaller and faster and it becomes a shimmy.

C. *The movement:* With shoulders near the floor, arms outstretched, back arched, and hips pushed up off the floor, twist the left hip up and forward.

D. Twist the right hip up and forward. Repeat this from left to right, making the movement smaller and faster to result in a very fast hip shimmy on the floor. Always keep your side to the audience when you do this movement.

THE ASCENT

What should you do when you've used all your floor tricks? Come up, of course. There's a technique to that, too, as in every other aspect of this beautiful dance. Whatever floor movement you complete, you must swing yourself into position to begin the ascent and return to your feet as gracefully as a fawn rising from a nap. *Follow the photos counterclockwise.*

A. The ascent begins from this position. Then, with your weight in your chest, bend from the hips—not the waist —and . . .

B. . . . raise your hips from the floor, always keeping your weight in your chest, and lean out over your right leg.

132

F. Pull up and forward with the chest, pushing off the right leg and returning to a standing position ready to proceed with any of the standing combinations you've already learned— or with the advance movements in the next chapter.

E. With your chest forward over your left leg and your left foot slightly turned out for balance, gracefully stretch your arms out to the back.

C. Pull up farther with your chest and come up on both knees.

D. Keep your weight on the right knee and bring the left leg forward.

A., B. As you slide your right leg down in back, reach the left hand under the skirt, as shown, and pull the skirt away from your legs and feet as you slowly descend to the floor.

MANAGING THE COSTUME

Learning to do the movements without tripping on the long, flowing yards of skirt material is essential. To gracefully move up and down without tripping on your swirling skirt requires certain hand movements that must be dance movements, too. It's not enough to simply reach, lift, and adjust your skirt; you must keep the arm and body movements flowing as you manipulate the costume away from your legs.

These are the same movements you learned in the Floor Descent (page 112) and the Ascent (page 132), and they should be practiced with the skirt until it flows and swirls and billows.

134

C. While the left leg is bent, before sliding it down, put your right hand under the skirt, pull it up, and throw it in back.

D. Place the right hand on the floor; continue to slide back and ease yourself all the way down.

E. The front skirt panel should be out in front over the left leg. The back panel should be all the way in back, free of your left leg and right hand.

Once on the floor, you may do any or all of the movements described, always swirling and swishing the fabric so you don't trip. Remember that the ascent and descent are done slowly, allowing you to stop at any point and intersperse subtle Shoulder Shimmies, Snake Arm movements, and other combinations that you can make part of your individual repertoire.

A. Before you begin to lift the body, use an arm movement, leading with the shoulder and following through with the body. Pull the back panel of the skirt behind you with the left hand. The right hand pulls the front panel forward and free of the legs.

B. As you rise and manipulate the skirt away from your legs, lean forward with the right shoulder . . .

E. . . . and continue to lead up with the right shoulder, following through with the arm movement, until you are all the way up, the skirt falls naturally down around your hips and thighs, and you are ready to sway into your next position.

D. As your left arm follows its up-and-forward movement, bring your left leg through the skirt opening . . .

C. . . . and continue upward, shifting the lead to the left shoulder and allowing the skirt to fall naturally.

Dahlena performs a hip
shimmy and Hip Drop simultaneously during a performance.

CHAPTER 8

ADVANCED MOVEMENTS

Choreographers frequently refer to the dance as "sculpture in motion." The successful dancer thinks of herself not as a flat image seen only from the front in her mirror, but as a three-dimensional figure that is pleasing from all sides at all times. The advanced movements help to give this dimension to the dance.

Advanced movements are a combination of many steps you have learned so far. Now think of the body as moving in several directions simultaneously. Your torso moves up and down while the hips go back and forth, and all the while you may be traveling gracefully about the dance floor. You will combine a shimmy with a Hip Drop and a traveling step. You may perform a Camel Walk with the Body Roll and add the Abdomen Roll and Flutter. You'll find several new snake movements to spice up the standing and floor positions. And you'll learn when to do the spin—for a vision of swirling, twisting chiffon and body.

The traveling steps and miscellaneous movements that follow may be used during a dance in the same sequence illustrated; but feel free to select any one or more that you like to expand a combination you already have created. You can refer to the suggested combinations in chapter 10 for a start and then choreograph your own dance. Remember, these movements, as all others, must be filled with energy— strong and controlled, yet smooth and flowing.

TRAVELING HIP ROLL

In this first traveling step, the Traveling Hip Roll, you negotiate a beautiful hip-rolling motion while you are moving around in a large open circle. First break down the movement and then smooth it out so it is done in two counts: 1) step out and roll; and 2) step forward. Begin with both knees bent slightly.

A. Place your weight on the right leg and extend the left leg in front with the knee bent further.

B. With a rolling motion, twist the left hip up and forward and hold. Do not turn the foot. Do not drop the hip.

C. Lift the left foot up and then step forward. Shift the weight to the left foot.

D. Bring the right leg in front, the right knee bent further.

E. Twist and roll the right hip up and hold. Lift the right foot, bringing the right hip up again. Repeat from A.

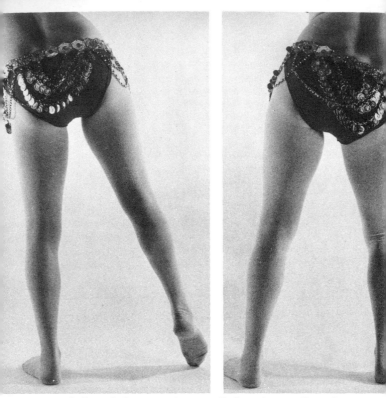

A. Lift the right hip up and out.

B. Step down and put the weight on the right foot; drop the right hip.

TRAVELING STEP: HIP DROP TURN

The Hip Drop Turn is a half-turn pivot that swings you from back to front as you travel in one direction across the stage. Follow the breakdown and then be sure the step is like this: begin with your back to the audience, step down, up down, and turn, facing the audience. Then repeat: down, up-down, turn, so your back is again to the audience.

D. Step onto the right leg again. Drop the right hip again, but this time keep the weight on the *right* foot.

C. Push the right leg and right hip up again, shifting the weight to the left leg.

E. Bring the left leg in front of the right as you pivot on the right foot. The left hip leads up to carry the left leg in front. Now you are facing forward. Count it as: *one, two, three, turn on four,* and change feet and pivot.

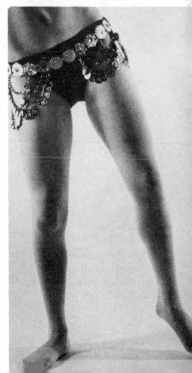

FRONT-BACK HIP DROP

The Front-Back Hip Drop is performed in place or as you walk backward during the medium-fast or fast music. Do a series of four or eight and then change to another step. Think of the count as: 1) drop right hip forward; 2) bring it back; 3) drop left hip forward; 4) bring it back. *Follow the photos counterclockwise.*

A. Extend the right leg out in front and push the right hip up.

B. Very important: keep the right heel off the floor; drop the right hip down away from the rib cage.

C. Push the right foot and hip up. Lead with the hip; bring the hip up and around in back and slightly out to the side.

144

F. Push the left hip up and around in back. Return to A and repeat.

E. Drop the right hip down, away from the rib cage.

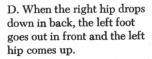

D. When the right hip drops down in back, the left foot goes out in front and the left hip comes up.

145

SIDE-TO-SIDE TRAVELER

The Side-to-Side Traveler enables you to move from side to side and around in a circle. It is like the Hip Lift (page 60), but now the feet take rapid little steps sideways or around in circles in time to the musical beat.

A. Step on the left leg and lift the right hip.

B. Step together.

 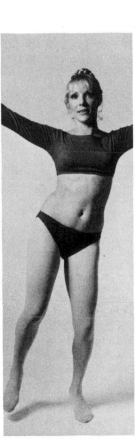

C. Lift the left hip.　　D. Lift the right hip and step together again.

HIP DROP WITH THE
SCOOTING SHIMMY

The Scooting Shimmy (page 53) is now combined with a Hip Drop to result in a rapid forward up-and-down movement that is done to medium-fast and fast music. Use it to move forward, around in a circle, and from one part of the stage to another in an arc, a diagonal, and the like.

A. The body is up on the toes, in the same position as the Scooting Shimmy. Begin the tiny forward foot movements and set the thighs in motion, back and forth alternately and quickly, then drop the left hip down when the left leg moves forward.

B. Drop the right hip when
the right leg moves forward.
Do this very rapidly as a
one-two; one-two beat. The
hips should be rapidly moving
up and down as you do the
Scooting Shimmy.

SNAKELIKE FLOOR DESCENT

Another method for descending verly slowly to the floor is by seemingly snaking your way down while your hands hypnotically perform the Front-Back Arm Movement (page 74). This descent is done very slowly. As you ascend, you can vary the arm movements. *Follow the photos counterclockwise.*

A. The arms snake front to back and the body sways slightly forward and back, echoing the arm movement.

B. Begin to descend . . .

C. . . . keeping your weight over your left leg and always moving the arms as though you are encircling a large ball and you can't get your arms close to your chest.

F. Pull all the way forward with the body weight over the left leg, always continuing the snaky arm movements. Rise up to position A and go on to another movement.

E. You can remain in this position for several counts and simply sway up and down while the arms command the center of interest. Lead up and forward with the chest and down and back with the shoulders.

D. Lean your shoulders back slightly, bending from the hips and keeping up the arm rhythm.

FIGURE EIGHT SNAKE

The Figure Eight Snake is another mesmerizing movement that provides variety to the choreography. It follows the large Hip Circle shown on page 62. Each time the hip moves in a Figure Eight, the body rises slightly for three counts and holds on the fourth count. Then you reverse the movement and snake down again. Repeat three or more times before ending with the Hip Circle (page 62), and progressing to another step.

A. When you complete the Hip Circle, you are in the position shown and ready to begin the Figure Eight Snake.

B. Bring your left leg in to the right leg, keeping the right hip up.

E. Push the left hip up and twist it slightly forward. Reverse movement by repeating positions D and C. When you have finished the number of up-and-down snakes desired . . .

D. Push the right hip up and twist it slightly forward.

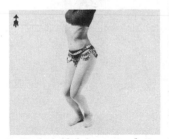

C. Push the left hip up and twist it slightly forward.

F. . . . step out with the left leg and continue into another large Hip Circle.

STACCATO HIP THRUST

A sharp, continuous movement is in direct contrast to the slow sinuous movements of the dancer and, as such, the Staccato Hip Thrust can serve as a transition from the medium-fast to the fast tempos. It can also be used with sharp drumbeats for about four to eight bars of music. For a doub. Staccato Hip Thrust, simply thrust the hip out and back twice on each side.

A. Place your weight on your right leg and drop your right hip . . .

B. . . . then use a sharp, quick movement and thrust the hip up and out.

C. Shift the weight to the
left leg with the
left hip dropped . . .

D. . . . and thrust the left hip
up and out to the left side.

HIP DROP ROTATION SWIVEL

The Hip Drop Rotation (page 56) is the basis for this advanced step—the Hip Drop Rotation Swivel—that could logically follow the Staccato Hip Thrust. It may be performed in one place, or it can be used as a subtle step forward or back by lifting and stepping with each foot as its hip moves. For this step, it is important that the accent is on the front forward position of the hip.

A. Arch your back slightly, bend both knees, and push the right hip up and forward.

B. Drop the right hip down in front. This should be accented as the strongest move in the series.

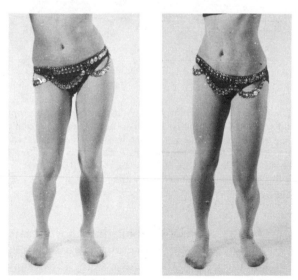

C. Push the right hip back up and drop it down in back at the same time you bring the left hip up and forward. Turn the left hip forward and . . .

D. . . . drop the left hip down in front with another accented beat. Push the left hip up and reverse from D to C to B to A. Repeat.

THE ABDOMEN ROLL AND FLUTTER

The ability to roll the abdomen from the top to the bottom and back up again is another example of how you can isolate and develop unused muscles into eye-boggling motions. First, practice the isolation below and then try the Abdomen Roll itself. It must be done while the breath is exhaled and held. This exercise is good for the waistline: if you do it about fifty times on and off every day, you could easily drop an inch from the waist and firm up the tummy.

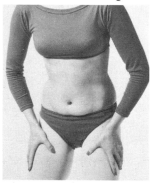 

A. *The exercise:* Bend slightly from the hips with the buttocks tight, knees bent, hands on thighs. Exhale. Stop the breath and hold. Push down against your thighs and suck in your stomach.

B. With the breath still stopped, *push* the stomach out (don't just let it out) and suck it in again. Repeat as many times as you can until you need another breath.

The Flutter develops from the above exercise. Breathe in and out with short, quick breaths—similar to a dog panting. Stop the breath. Using the abdomen, continue the same motion of fast breathing but without the breath. This requires concentration and practice. It is impossible to illustrate photographically. If you don't understand how it is done, watch a belly dancer and then practice it.

The Abdomen Roll usually is used during the slow tempos and combined with a Camel Walk and a Torso Roll (page 38) with the arms extended. Training the muscles properly may take weeks or months. Some people can never do it; but the practice is guaranteed to firm you up.

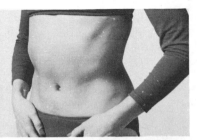

A. Breathe normally. Contract the muscles from the waist down and, at the same time, push out the muscles from the waist up.

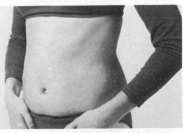

B. Push the muscles out from the waist down.

C. Contract the muscles from the waist up.

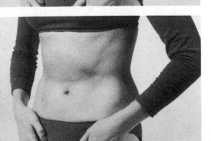

D. Contract the muscles from the waist down. Repeat from A.

159

TURNING, SPINNING

The turn, or spin, is always used at the finale of the dance. It is also a dramatic and beautiful transition between fast music and slower movements. Most people turn to the right. It is helpful to focus your

A. Step out onto the right foot. During the turn, take very small steps, always keeping the right foot in front of the left.

F. . . . until both the body and head are facing in the same direction. Take several turns. You may also spin around the floor so it becomes a traveling turn.

eyes on a spot so that your head turns properly; this will also prevent dizziness. Do the spin very slowly when you are learning it, first using eight small steps. Progress faster, spinning all around in four steps. Then turn in two steps—one leading you to the back and one returning you to the front. *Follow the pictures clockwise.*

B. As you turn toward the back, you may want to focus your eyes on a spot directly in front of you.

C. When the body is facing directly in back and the eyes are still on the spot, get ready to turn your head.

E. Continue to turn . . .

D. As you continue turning to the right, turn your head all the way around and find the same spot in front with your eyes.

 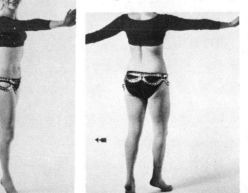

THE KARSHLIMAR

The *karshlimar* (Kahsh-le-MAH) is a Turkish folk dancing step often used in belly dancing during the

A. Step forward on your right foot.

D. Step forward onto the left foot.

E. Step back again onto the right foot.

medium-fast happy music. It is a perky, lilting, yet subtle hopping movement done to a nine-eight tempo; in every fourth bar there is an extra beat.

B. Bring the left leg from behind and lift it in front.

C. As you bring the left foot from back to front, contract the pelvis and skip on your right foot.

F. Bring the left foot back again.

G. Put your weight on the left foot; then, stepping forward on the right foot again, repeat from B.

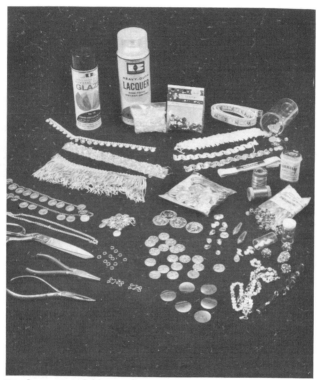

For decorating the bra and
hip band you will need a
variety of coins, beads,
spangles, chains, pieces of old
jewelry and jump rings, beaded
and fringed trims, needles,
heavy carpet threads or dental
floss, large hooks and eyes,
glue, scissors, pliers, and
transparent sprays.

CHAPTER 9

CREATING A COSTUME

In Middle Eastern countries, the ethnic dance costume is used for festivals, holidays, and weddings. The young woman of the house often entertains for visitors. Her costume may represent her dowry—a silver, gold and jewel-encrusted bra and hip band are a sign of wealth.

Luckily, you can make a costume just for the fun of it. Many women who begin to dance "for the exercise" graduate to a skirt and chain belt. Soon they bead and bangle a bra and hip band. Whether you plan to dance for yourself, for your own shiek, or for a group, making a costume can be an absorbing, creative challenge. If you have doubts about how exposed you want to be or about body scars showing—don't worry—costumes can be devised to cover everything yet give the·necessary illusions.

Only four basic parts are required for the costumes: the bra, hip band, skirt, and veil (described in chapter 5). Ideas for making costumes are offered, but be innovative and daring; as the dance becomes modern and eclectic, so may the costume.

With your costume you will need sheer panty hose, support stockings, or tights. Over these, wear bikini dance trunks of heavy Helanca stretch fabric—available from dance suppliers in flesh tones and in colors to match your costume. Wear dance shoes, Cleopatra or other sandals, or bare feet.

Long hair is traditional because it carries through the fluidity of the dance and may be more sensuous. Flattering hair pieces may be added, but any style, short or long, with which you are comfortable, is fine.

MAKING THE BRA AND THE HIP BAND

The bra and hip band usually match in coloring and trim. The bra, designed to flatter the figure and make it voluptuous, is made from a hard-shell bra that you cut apart and decorate. Select a half-bra (the amount of padding will depend on your figure) made of a heavy cotton or satin fabric. Cut apart and re-cover as shown, then decorate with beads, coins, chains, fringe, and the like. To prevent tarnishing, always spray the coins and metal parts with lacquer, plastic acrylic spray, or clear nail polish. Beads should be sewn on with carpet thread or dental floss. Glue them in place and then sew them; the action of the dance tends to loosen any beads that are only glued.

Avoid elastic shoulder straps for the bra as they do not hold the bust secure enough during the dance. Use elastic across the back to allow for breathing, but cover it with matching fabric made as a tube that fits over the elastic and permits it to stretch.

The costume bra is made by cutting apart and removing the straps from a lingerie bra. The cups and straps can be refit so the bust has a voluptuous look. Tip the cups up and out at the sides of the breast, leaving a space between the breasts. The cups can be connected by chain or covered fabric and then decorated. For well-endowed dancers, a wired bra can be decorated and the straps can be redesigned. .

Cover each cup with a satin
fabric or with silver or gold
lamé. Pin in tucks. Allow
ample fabric to cover the
inside, too.

It is important that the strap design for the costume
not look like a lingerie bra. Observe designs in the costumes shown. Plagiarize details from costumes used in
television and movie musicals, from opera costumes,
from dance magazines, and from paintings and sculptures showing clothing from ancient Egypt, Greece,
and India. Research library books on costumes and
jewelry to spark ideas for original creations. Observe
the necklines and strap designs in evening and beach-
wear illustrated in current sewing pattern books.

If you have abdominal scars, design the bra with
multiple strands of chains and bangles hanging from
the bottom. Heavy pancake makeup can help camou-
flage marks. Dance supply companies sell flesh-
colored, very sheer, sleeveless body stockings that may
be worn under the bra and skirt (with your long hair
and/or collarlike necklaces, no one will see the
stocking).

Smooth the covering fabric
and pin all the way around, as
shown. Then stitch in tucks
and sew covering to cup. The
cup at left shows an extra satin
interlining that will be basted
inside the covered cup. This
allows you to replace the lining
if it becomes soiled.

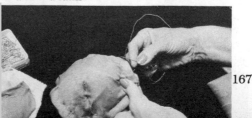

What about a jewel in the navel? Forget it. It is impractical, and there's no way to make it stay in place.

The hip band may be as simple or as ornate as you like. A beginner might use two layers of three-inch-wide drapery trim in two colors (gold over silver), sewn to a length of elastic and worn beneath a chain belt. Heavily beaded fabrics may be found on old dresses in secondhand and rummage shops, and these fabrics can be cut or improvised to fit on a stiff Pellon or scrim backing. Glittery fabrics in a staggering variety can be found wherever costume materials are sold and often in general fabric marts. Cut a paper pattern to fit your hip size and shaped the way you like. Then transfer to the Pellon and fabric, allowing ¾ inch for hems and enough of a tab for closing with sturdy hooks and eyes.

A hand-beaded hip band and unfinished bra. The front of the band (at right) is shaped with a dip and with longer, more elaborate strands of bugle beads than those used around the back. The hip band is decorated with various teardrop and round glass stones, strands of different sized seed pearls, crystals, and bugle beads.

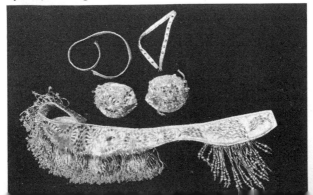

Dahlena's costume bra is covered with silver lamé and composed mainly of chains in a unique arrangement. The band is silver, jeweled with glass stones. A silver chain belt is worn over the band.

Necklaces, arm bracelets, head
jewelry, and ankle bracelets
are important accessories for
an exotic look.

*Jewelry, courtesy
The Rams Boutique,
Wilmette, Illinois*

Belts are available in many designs and materials, such as brass, pearls, silver and gold chains, and coins. Wear one or more with your hip band. You can make one belt wider by adding parts of other belts.

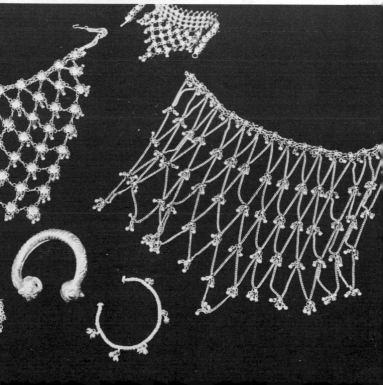

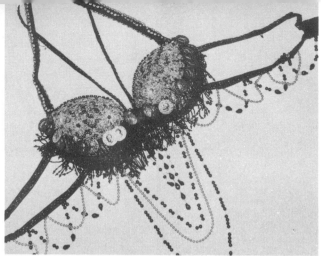

This bra is covered with black fabric, black beaded straps, and coins. Note how the cups are tilted sideways and the bra straps redesigned with lengths of beading added.

The hip band, over a black chiffon skirt, echoes the design and materials of the bra. The chains are draped so that they are longer in front and gradually become shorter at the sides and around the back.

The costume, all put together,
is made of bugle beads. This
basic form may be embellished
in thousands of ways.

173

MAKING THE SKIRT

The sway and swish of the filmy skirt is feminine and lovely. You'll probably want to make a skirt to practice with, and you can use it as the basis for your costume. As you begin to put together costume parts, you'll be amazed that there is more fabric and more of you covered up during this "very sensual" dance than the average costume worn by a chorus girl. You are much less exposed than the majority of women on the beaches and in many television programs.

The skirt design varies. Some women are happy using a three-to-four-yard length of fabric—knotted on one side at the hips with a slit over one leg. But the chiffon skirt with panels—through which both legs have complete freedom—is more graceful and follows the undulations of the body movements you have tried so diligently to perfect.

The skirt panels can be made from a circle, as shown at right, or from lengths of material gathered onto a heavy elastic waistband. (See photos on the following pages.) The only criterion for the fabric is that it should hang freely and be soft and flowing. A nylon chiffon is good, but it does tend to snag. Rayon chiffon is not serviceable because it hangs out of shape. Polyester crepe chiffon is preferred and very durable. Sheer curtain materials may be used. Sari cloth with fine nailheads or silk stitching is costly and scarce, but it makes a magnificent costume. The skirt length should reach the top of the shoe—it should never be so long that you trip on it.

A full skirt of two or more colors can be devised by using two layers of fabric attached to two separate bands or by having different colored panels.

The following directions and fabric requirements are for a skirt about 36 inches finished length for a girl about five feet six inches tall. Use 45-inch or 54-

inch-wide fabric 6¾ yards long. You will also need a length of bias tape and a length of 2- to 2½-inch-wide grosgrain ribbon 1½ times the circumference of your hips.

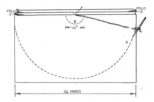

1. Fold the fabric in thirds to form three layers, 2¼ yards each. Lay flat. At the center top of the material pin a string long enough to reach the outer edge of the bottom of the material. Tie a pencil on the end of the string and draw a half circle (A) on the material. Cut through all three layers at once to yield three half circles.

2. Cut a small half circle at line B (at top) a distance of about 10 inches between the two points. This edge will be gathered and sewn to a length of bias tape for the hip band.

3. Sew two of the half circles together to form the back skirt panel. Run a basting stitch along the top to gather before stitching on tape. Also run a basting stitch through the top of the remaining half circle which will be the front panel.

4. Measure your hips with a length of bias tape and tie around your hips. Mark the position of the half circles; the back panel should come around the sides to the front. Between the back and front panels, leave a space of about two inches over each leg.

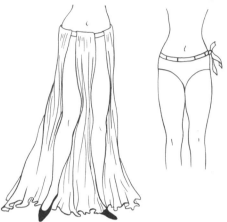

5. Pin the gathered top of the panels to the bias tape; then stitch.

6. Use a length of grosgrain ribbon. Stitch one edge over the gathered fabric just below the bias tape as you would the waistband on a skirt.

7. Fold tape up over the gathers and stitch the other edge onto the skirt back so the gathers and tape are enclosed under the ribbon. (Use ribbon that matches the fabric.)

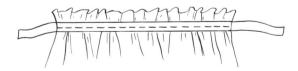

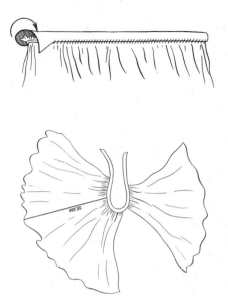

8. To allow the bias to stretch, let the finished skirt hang for two or three days before hemming. Make a narrow rolled hem by hand or machine.

9. For a fuller, more flowing skirt, use nine yards of fabric folded three times to form four layers. Sew three half circles together to form the back panel, and use one half circle for the front.

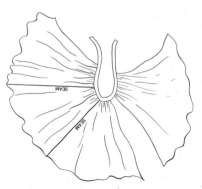

The waistband of the tights
and panty hose should be
rolled down below the tummy
and the first layer of skirt
wrapped around.

There is a technique to putting on a costume properly. This series of photographs illustrates the layers
as well as the way the costume is made.

The second skirt panel is placed over the first. This can be made of the same color or of different colors. Observe the spacing of the chiffon on the band. It's better not to sew the decorated hip band and skirt together. That way you can use the band over different skirts, and it makes cleaning and steaming more practical.

A fabric hip band can be pulled tightly around the buttocks and hips and tied in front. This band is usually worn under chain belts rather than under beaded hip bands. The band should be pinned through the skirts to the tights at the back, to prevent it from sliding up as you dance. When a beaded hip band is worn, it, too, should be anchored to the tights so it doesn't ride up.

Costumes used for nightclub
performances often utilize
materials that will glisten under
spotlights. At the beginning
of the dance, Dena's sequined-
and-print veil is draped by
tucking two corners under the
bra·straps. No matter how the
veil is draped, the arms should
remain free to move. The use
of a veil is optional.

An ethnic costume from Egypt is made of a fine black net fabric with tiny rectangular silver nailheads throughout. Any adaptation of it is perfect for women who do not want to expose their midriffs. The front opening may be closed and a body stocking or flesh-colored bra worn beneath. A wide hip band of solid-colored fabric is tied low on the hips, and a chain belt is worn over the band. The dancer may be barefoot: smooth ankle bracelets can be worn. A jewel may be pasted in the center of the forehead.

Costume, Salma Angres Collection, Wilmette, Illinois

Katherina wears a handmade
costume completely covered
with pearls on the bra and
band. A double strand of pearls
around her waist and hips adds
an individual touch.

Natasha's unusually designed
"veil" coat goes around her
neck and is almost backless;
the back is cut below the waist.
It is graceful, flows easily, and
is simple to remove during
the dance.

A pair of midriff harem pajamas makes an interesting costume as wicked and wild as Scheherazade herself. Harem pants are available from the firm listed in the Supply Sources and from some lingerie shops. They can be easily improvised from a pattern for hostess pants in such sewing magazines as *Vogue, Simplicity,* or the like. Adjust the pattern so the waist is shorter and stops at the hip. The wide legs can have elastic in the hems to give them a bloused look. Or make the legs about fourteen inches longer than the pattern calls for. Pull the elastic hem to your knee so a full blouse effect hangs to the ankles.

Two other ideas for harem
pants could be taken from
these costume designs by Leon
Bakst for the ballets *Le Dieu
Bleu* and *Scheherazade*.

A fourth-century A.D. stone sculpture of an Indian maiden is rich in images that could spark costume ideas. Observe the neckpieces, wrist coils, hip band, and accordion-pleated skirt. Arts and crafts from Thailand, ancient Greece, Persia; paintings from Renaissance, Venetian, and neoclassic artists; and figures on oriental scrolls offer an unending variety of clothing and jewelry images. Study the draping on stone carvings from tenth- and eleventh-century Romanesque churches and the jewels on Balinese dancers. Pore over ancient and contemporary costume books. Take time to look at available fabrics from theatrical fabric specialists or in the novelty yard goods department of a fabric mart.

Designs for an asymmetrical top could be derived from an ancient bacchante's dress or a dancer's costume.

CHAPTER 10

PUTTING IT TOGETHER— TO MUSIC

Once you smooth the first few exercises into dance movements, you'll begin to lift and sway your hips whenever you hear an American or Middle Eastern selection that has the characteristic belly dance beat. We have suggested that your practice sessions be accompanied by music. Now it's time to stop and listen to what happens to the beat and how the music changes in different parts of a song; it's time to think about how you can accompany the music by combining the dance movements you have learned.

When the famous choreographer George Balanchine was asked, "How do you go about developing a ballet?" he answered, "I know the music; I choose it; I listen to it. I listen, listen, listen, listen and then it comes; the general idea of what I want. . . . The dance is like building a sculpture. You have the clay there and you work on it, molding it, changing it, shaping it, until you have what you want."

WHAT TO LISTEN FOR

Therein lies the secret of choreography—whether it's ballet or belly dancing. You must listen to the music and analyze it. When you know what melodies, what moods, what beats will follow one another, you can begin to think about "performing" a dance. No one can teach you how to personally interpret the music and develop your own style. But you can learn how to analyze the music, what to listen for, and how to begin with certain basic slow and fast combinations and build onto these as you like.

Music is written to display and create moods. These moods are marked by the changes in the rhythms, tones, and tempos of a song. You are probably aware of this from American songs you have listened to from childhood. The song begins with a melody which is altered by tone and tempo two or three times within the central portion. The end of the song usually returns to the original melody. A musician, singer, or dancer may interpret these melodies in different ways, repeating one or more portions at various intervals—whether or not the music is written that way.

Most people can listen to, feel, and anticipate the moments for changing the dance combinations. If you feel you lack this innate ability for interpretation, you will have to study sheet music and listen carefully to the phrasing in recorded selections until you can recognize the musical components. The same factors that you pick out of any music—American, Spanish, Polish, or Irish—apply to Middle Eastern music.

ANALYZING MIDDLE EASTERN MUSIC

Middle Eastern music sounds exotic and appealing to the Western ear—partly because of the Eastern quarter-tone scale which has delicate nuances and subtleties. The music tells a story and changes moods as it moves through gay, painful, sad, and penetrating melodies. The dancer acts out these moods with her body, her expression, her charm, and her personality.

Interestingly, most Middle Eastern music is improvised as the musicians play their special instruments. Unless the sounds are captured on records, it is unlikely that the same music will ever be repeated exactly. When musicians accompany a dancer, she and they work together, developing and improvising the moods. Of course, having the sounds captured on records enables you to listen to the same music repeatedly and to work out a dance combination.

The first aspect of the music you should listen for is the beat—which you can tap out with your fingers or with your zills. The music is basically a four-count rhythm that is either sped up or slowed down. Think of the heavy, solid beat as Ā and the faster beats as TEK.

Do the TEK with the right-hand finger cymbals and the Ā with the left-hand finger cymbals.
Basic 4-4 time:

TEK-Ā-TEK TEK-Ā-TEK TEK-Ā-TEK
TEK-Ā-TEK

Single pattern:

TEK Ā TEK Ā TEK Ā TEK Ā TEK Ā
TEK Ā TEK Ā TEK

Regardless of the differences in rhythm (and these rhythms vary in individual songs), the entire composition can be analyzed by its different parts. Remember, the purpose of the music is to convey moods, so the music is broken into portions that portray these moods, changing from one mood to another and back again. The two basic divisions are referred to as the *chefta-telli* and the *taxim* and the music bounces back and forth from these divisions after a fast introduction.

Chefta-telli (chif-te-TEL-ee) is a Turkish word. The instruments, accompanying one another, play a gay, happy, mood-setting music using any of the beats and in any of the tempos—slow, medium-fast, or fast. The dancer reacts to the music and changes her steps and movements accordingly. (You will also come across the word *beledi* [BELL-ed-ee], an Arabic word that refers to the same portion of the music as the *chefta-telli*.) One song will have one, two, or more *chefta-telli* portions, indicating the alternation of moods with the *taxim*.

Taxim (TOX-eem) is an improvised portion of the music. That means no written music exists for it. The drum stops and the oud (or the violin) becomes the solo sound. The musician ad-libs the way he feels at the moment. He plays a solo that is very serious, sad—almost spine tingling in its emotional depth. He improvises, based on feelings that emanate from the depths of the heart, and he may vocally chant soulful, doleful, wailing sounds. He may be accompanied with a distant-sounding strain by a flute or a clarinet. The rhythm is usually slow at the beginning and may build up to medium-fast and fast passages, then back to the slow portions.

What is the dancer doing during the *taxim?* Usually she has descended to the floor, and she interprets the sounds with the seriousness they require. She performs the various floor movements—slowly leaning back and coming forward while her snakelike arm positions spell out the doleful mood of the chant. When she has completed the floor movements, she will rise, and that will be the cue for the *taxim* to end.

The music may then shift to another *chefta-telli* portion, to a drum solo, or to another blend of music for several minutes. Another *taxim* portion may be performed but this time with less intensity or seriousness. Usually the dancer does not perform a second floor routine; rather she emphasizes the slow movements and portrays the mood with a serious expression.

In this way, the song progresses, switching from gay, playful melodies to sad, sorrowful improvised solos and back again to happy moods. Experienced dancers and musicians take their cues from one another. They may improvise *taxims.* They may add a fast encore, the drummer and the dancer performing a duet. The Ā-TEK-TEKS underscore and deliciously accompanying the clanging cymbals, jangling coins, swirling skirts, and the magnetic movement of the body—deliberately titillating, always in control, and spinning to a high, ecstatic finale with the audience clapping for more.

NOW TO DANCE

With the musical composition broken down to bite-sized beats and divisions, you are ready to put together the step combinations. Remember, you need not know a great variety of steps. Many dancers use only three or four movements, but they pepper these with so many changes that it would be hard to recognize any repetition. They use improvisational flourishes, change the direction and size of the steps, alter hip movements with arm and hand displays, and shift the tension and dynamics of their bodies. They change moods and speed with the music; and they use the veil, the tilt of their head, and their personality to keep from being bored or boring.

On the following pages, one slow and one fast combination are offered to help you begin. The average professional performance lasts fifteen to twenty minutes. Each combination illustrated will take two to three minutes. So the entire performance is a series of such combinations—repeated, built upon, improvised, and varied throughout the dance with different tempos. One secret of successful choreography is not to give away all you know in the first part of the dance; save some of your spectacular movements to reveal as the dance unfolds.

Beginning Combination for Slow Music

8 Traveling Hip Rolls	Around in a large open circle.	Page 140
4 Figure Eights	To regular time.	Page 24
4 Figure Eights	To double time and in one place.	Page 24
4 Camel Walk Rocks	Side to side—regular time.	Page 34
4 Figure Eights	Regular time—in place.	Page 24
4 Figure Eights	Double time—can be down, down, and up.	Page 152
Backward Camel Walk	Can be done as a rocking step or a single step	

Vary this combination with veil movements, by using finger cymbals, and by interspersing other steps as you become proficient.

When preparing a combination for a performance, it is often helpful to write down the combinations, as above, until you can move into them in a practiced, intuitive manner.

Beginning Combination for Fast Music

8	Side Hip Thrusts. Single; one on each side. Feet together.	Page 48
4 to 8	Up-and-Down Shimmies	Page 46
	Hip Drop with a Scooting Shimmy around in a large circle.	Page 148
	Complete the circle facing front.	
4	Hip Drops in place.	Page 54
4	Side-to-Side Hip Drops	Page 58
	Return to	
4	Up-and-Down Shimmies with feet together and finish with a spin.	Page 50 / Page 160
	Then change, with the music, into a slow combination or into the floor movements, as required.	

The fast combinations may be accompanied by the cymbals. These combinations are simply a basis on which to build your individual interpretation and routine.

Following are suggested steps to use with different portions of the music:

Medium Fast: This is the entry; to which you may do:
Traveling steps
Hip thrusts
Hip shimmies
Transition—a spin and change to

Slow: Figure Eight and variations
Camel Walk and variations with an Abdomen Roll
Subtle Shoulder Shimmy
Subtle hip shimmies
Any of the arm and snake movements alone and with body movements
Veil movements
The tempo picks up and changes to

Fast:	Repeat steps used in the medium fast but speed up the beat. The exception: do not use the Camel Walk, Figure Eight, and similar movements that are effective for supple, fluid beauty only when they are done slowly. In this portion repeat and vary some of the steps you used at the beginning and change their progression. *Transition—spin and change to*
Very Slow:	This is the dramatic tempo performed to the *taxim*. End the spin by descending to the floor and performing any or all of the floor movements. Always intersperse the more difficult, vibrant shimmies and sways with quiet moments, and let only your hands and arms set the mood of the haunting improvised strains of the solo instruments. Near the end of the slow tempo, begin your ascent. *Continue a few standing slow movements until the tempo picks up and becomes*
Medium-Fast and Fast:	This is a happy, bouncy, folklike music which calls for: Traveling Hip Drops Large Scooting Shimmies in circles Side-to-side lifts in circles *Continue until you near the*
Finale:	A fast tempo using: Scooting Shimmies Rapid shimmies Hip thrusts Finish with a fast spin. *Stop and take a bow.*

A few additional notes:

- The belly dance depends for its beauty on body form and movements in a comparatively confined area. It does not require leaps and glides across the stage as do many other dance forms.

- The belly dance is sensual rather than sexual. It is not coy or flirtatious. It is provocative but promises nothing. It is designed to give pleasure for its own sake. It should be performed with dignity and an air of classicism; it must never be vulgar or crude.

- Your facial expressions should reflect the mood of the music. Be serious during the slow, sad parts. Reflect a happy, delicious excitement in the gay parts.

- Use your eyes to carry through the movement and the mood. Let the eyes follow the slide of the head; concentrate on the snaky movements of the arms; appear dreamy and moody or gay and vivacious. Never watch your feet or your navel.

- Your mouth, too, adds to the expressiveness of the total mood; let it break into an inviting smile, a pouting purse, or a soft Mona Lisa parting of the lips. Never have a smile pasted or frozen on your face.

- Always be conscious of your position in relation to your audience. Especially in the floor movements, keep your side, rather than your knees, to the audience.

- When your hands do touch your body, never stroke your thighs or your bosom. Never adjust your costume as you dance.

- If you forget a practiced combination, don't panic. Simply remain poised: the moving sculpture is entitled to stop, to pause, to give the audience a chance to catch its breath, and to give you time to remember or improvise. Such frozen moments

197

when you feel you are doing nothing may seem interminable, but they usually pass unnoticed or appear as a part of the dance.

MIDDLE EASTERN INSTRUMENTS

An early identification of the various Middle Eastern musical instruments will increase your appreciation of the music and your ability to pick out the different sounds. Observe the actual instruments when you attend dance performances; look for illustrations on record jackets. Try to learn which instruments make which sounds.

The *oud* (ood), pictured on page 199, is a lutelike instrument with six double strings and a fingerboard without frets. It is also similar to a mandolin—which could be tuned to sound like an oud. The oud strings are made of goat gut and are plucked with an eagle feather. It produces soulful, hauting sounds.

The *darbouka* (dar-boo-KA) is also called the *durbeki* or *dumbeg*. It is a traditional drum of the Middle East and is made in two parts that produce two basic counts: the flat vibration that results in the DUM and the sharper, more metallic sound that is the TEK.

The *bazooki* (ba-ZOOK-ee) is a lutelike stringed instrument with a pear-shaped sound box that produces a more metallic sound than the oud.

The *kanoon* (kah-NOON) is an Arabic and Turkish seventy-two-stringed instrument that looks like a zither. It is played with picks placed on the tips of the index fingers. It has a sound similar to, but mellower than, the zither.

The *santour* (san-TOOR) is a Persian zither with metal strings that are struck with small mallets. It has frets and resembles a xylophone.

Natasha begins the floor movements to Tony Karagozian's improvised oud solo during the *taxim* portion of the music.

CHAPTER 11

THE PROFESSIONAL ATTITUDE

As interest in Middle Eastern dancing is piqued, those who are smitten with its loveliness carry their message to others. Many women talk glowingly about the dance and tell their friends of the changes it has made in their outlook. Some women become so proficient that they are anxious to perform, and they are encouraged to do so.

Once you decide to put on a show for an audience —other than your favorite man or personal friends— you are apt to become involved in some professional situations. Indeed, you may eventually become a professional. To help you avoid the mishaps of less forewarned sisters, you should be armed with a proper professional attitude.

Your total attitude should be that the dance is an art form, that you are an artist. Always promote the dance on its highest level whether you are dancing in someone's house or in a nightclub.

When you are beginning, you may find some of your best experience dancing with other girls for benefit performances, arranged either by your teacher or by one of the dancers. Many teachers are asked to have their students dance for high school and college dance classes, for Golden Age groups, or for special parties in hospitals and charity institutions. Such performances are in good taste and help to educate the public to the inherent grace of the belly dance as art.

With this experience you may gain the confidence to perform by yourself. The following list of *dos* and *don'ts* is offered as a guide.

Helena conveys an attitude
of pride and seriousness about
the dance.

201

1. When you accept an engagement, be sure you have your combinations well rehearsed so you can present an energetic fifteen-to-seventeen-minute performance. Begin with small shows until you are confident that you have enough stage experience to perform for a large group under lights and with professional musicians.

2. The best engagements for the beginner are house parties, but be sure the guests are couples, not stags.

3. Always clarify the musical accompaniment you will have, whether records, tapes, or musicians. Confirm that the necessary equipment will be provided. If you are to bring records, the record player should be provided. Know beforehand what music will accompany you.

4. Always make the financial arrangement clear before any performance. Agree to be paid when you are finished. Have a written agreement stating the date, time, place, approximate length of performance, accompaniment, and fee. If the person who is hiring you does not provide the form, write one in duplicate and have it signed.

5. If you are working through an agent, the agent handles the financial arrangements. Select a reputable agent. Before signing with one or more agents, ask to speak to some of his or her other clients. Call them for a reference and ask if the agent provides dancing dates at reputable places and whether the dancer is paid promptly.

6. During the heyday of cabaret belly dancing, nightclub owners paid the dancers a minimal amount of money and encouraged them to go through the audience and collect tips by having the guests put money in the dancers' bras and hip bands. This cus-

tom tends to lower the level of the dance. It is better to ask for money for your performance than to accept tips. (Some cabaret operators ask for a cut of the tips.)

7. Some women's clubs hold auditions for performers once a year. At this time program chairmen for many organizations view the acts that they may book for programs throughout the year. Such auditions are five-to-eight-minute performances and they are a welcome way to become known. Restaurants and nightclubs may request an audition if they plan to book you for a standing engagement. One five-minute audition is not unreasonable. But if you are wanted for only one performance, an audition should not be encouraged. If you are asked to give one performance free, as an audition for future engagements, be sure you know the reputation of the people who are asking. Some clubs use this ploy to get free performances and then rarely hire the entertainers for repeat shows.

8. You should have one good publicity photo of yourself in costume that can be used to publicize your performances. You can have multiple copies made very reasonably (about ten or fifteen cents each) by photo processors who specialize in this work—not by the usual film processor. Check the classified pages of your phone book. Guests sometimes take photos at parties and clubs. You are free to ask for what purpose the photos are being taken and to insist that they never be used for publication. If someone does indicate they want to publish a photo, either do not grant permission or insist on seeing the photo before giving permission, and set a time limit. This is to protect yourself from someone taking photos in unflattering poses and using them indiscriminately for advertising or other purposes.

9. Never lower your standards just to get a job.

10. Always be on time.

With these points clarified, you can concentrate on your performance—a performance that will emphasize your attitude toward the dignity and delight of the dance.

During the slow movements, Helena expresses beauty in the movement of the veil, the angle of her body, and the tilt of her head.

Natasha personifies the mood of the music itself during the slow, serious part of the song as the singer chants to his improvised accompaniment on the oud.

205

Maya's position—body, head,
and arms held high—reflects
the dignity and attitude of the
Middle Eastern dancer.

Natasha plays her zills to the
beat of the oud and the
darbouka during the gay,
happy rhythms.

The portions of the *chefta-telli* are interpreted by Dahlena, left and right, and by Maya, below.

Nadia reflects the free-swirling, joyous spirit of the dance.

After her twirl and bow, Dahlena acknowledges the work of her musician, Joe Lazar.

SUPPLY SOURCES

Middle Eastern Dance Supplies   records, belts,
7002 N. Clark St.   cymbals, veils,
Chicago, Illinois 60626   skirts, jewelry
(Send self-addressed envelope for price list)

Scheherazade   harem pants
4608 Winchester
Memphis, Tennessee 38118
(Send self-addressed envelope for price list)

ABOUT THE AUTHORS

Dahlena's dance teaching methods, professional performances, and artistic attitude toward Middle Eastern dancing have been widely acknowledged from coast to coast during the past twelve years. Her early ballet training in Portland, Oregon resulted in engagements that took her to Boston and New York where she met the Middle Eastern dancers, Princess Yasmina from Algeria and the Jamal Twins from Egypt. She was attracted by the slow, sinuous, and beautiful movements and by the mood-setting music. Although she is an American, her unusual ability to perform the Middle Eastern dance earned her a reputation in many cities—including Las Vegas where she was asked to choreograph a show. She had to break down the movements to teach them to other dancers.

Dahlena's expertise quickly spread and, as Americans began to discover Greek, Turkish, and Arabic restaurants, her approach to the dance as a healthy and liberating art form won interest and admiration. A group of Chicago suburban women asked her to teach. Their response was so phenomenal that she subsequently opened studios in two Chicago locations. She has trained many teachers in the Dahlena methods.

Dahlena has taught masters' classes and been a guest teacher at numerous colleges and universities. She resides in Chicago with her two young children, Angela and Joseph.

Dona Z. Meilach is a nationally known author-photographer of more than twenty-five how-to-do-it trend setting art and craft books including *Macrame: Creative Design in Knotting, Contemporary Batik and Tie-Dye,* "*Soft Sculpture,*" and others. She writes a syndicated column on crafts and her articles on a wide variety of subjects have appeared in hundreds of national magazines.

Dona became intrigued by the exercise aspects of belly dancing when a foot injury forced her to give up tennis. Belly dancing firmed up her body and made her feel better and more flexible than any form of exercise she had tried. After studying with several teachers, she discovered Dahlena and her logical, gradual process for teaching the dance, not through memorized routines but through total body conditioning. Dona lives in a Chicago suburb with her husband. She has a son in college and a married daughter.

Bantam Book Catalog

It lists over a thousand money-saving best-sellers originally priced from $3.75 to $15.00 —bestsellers that are yours now for as little as 60¢ to $2.95!

The catalog gives you a great opportunity to build your own private library at huge savings!

So don't delay any longer—send us your name and address and 25¢ (to help defray postage and handling costs).
